Tools of the Maritime Trades

TOOLS OF THE MARITIME TRADES

JOHN E. HORSLEY

David & Charles
Newton Abbot London Vancouver

British Library Cataloguing in Publication Data

Horsley, John E.
Tools of the maritime trades.
1. Ship-building – Great Britain – Tools and
implements – History 2. Ships-Equipment and
supplies – History
I. Title
623.8'3   VM901

ISBN 0–7153–5280–6

Set in Baskerville
by Trade Linotype Limited, Birmingham
and printed in Great Britain
by Redwood Burn Limited, Trowbridge and Esher
for David & Charles (Publishers) Limited
Brunel House Newton Abbot Devon

Published in Canada
by Douglas David & Charles Limited
1875 Welch Street North Vancouver BC

CONTENTS

LIST OF PLATES

INTRODUCTION

The accepted fate of those who work behind the scenes is to remain unsung and forgotten, to vanish into obscurity. Thus it is with the craftsmen of Britain's maritime trades, whose contribution to her maritime history was prodigious, yet is almost forgotten. The names of a few of the master shipwrights of the past have come down to us, chiefly those concerned with the construction of the larger and more important fighting ships, and we know that Hawkins, the Plymouth merchant, played an important rôle in the improvement of the British fleet a few years before the Spanish Armada attacked in 1588. Yet even the best known of the master craftsmen remains virtually anonymous compared with those who used his products—Drake, Grenville, Davis, Nelson and many more.

During the great days of wooden ships, indeed as far back as the fifteenth century, English shipwrightry was widely envied. Perhaps one of the finest tributes to English craftsmanship was paid during the seventeenth century, when it was said that although French designs were superior, a copy built by English shipwrights was by far the better ship. This says little for English designing, of course, though this was improved by importing leading Italian and Venetian designers to instruct the English in their techniques. It appears, however, that the work of the French designers of the seventeenth century suffered at the hands of her shipwrights, who were reportedly unable to build two identical ships from one design. With the relatively primitive methods then in use, this might seem less surprising than the quality achieved in Britain. Even so, it became something of a joke in contemporary British shipyards, and many French prize vessels were practically rebuilt on their original lines in English and Scottish yards for use in the British navy.

The intention of this book is to catalogue and illustrate as many as possible of the tools which were used in the various maritime trades. It

became apparent during efforts to identify items in the collection of shipbuilding tools in Brixham Museum that no suitable reference book was available; some of the information was still available from very elderly craftsmen, but it soon became clear that their knowledge had its limitations. Few of them had experience of tools used outside their own circle of work, and the scope of work, which was more limited than was at first envisaged, varied tremendously from man to man, depending upon a wide range of factors. Principal among these was the yard or yards where he had worked, and the type of work in which each yard specialised. He might have worked on small boats, larger sailing ships such as schooners or fishing craft, or in the Naval Dockyards. He might have spent his whole life doing one kind of job such as building clench-built open boats, or perhaps he worked as a spar-maker, as many shipwrights did. No single shipwright was able to list for me the full range of tools in use during the period 1900–10, partly because of the factors listed above, and partly because of the introduction of power tools in some places and not in others. While one yard might have used earlier methods powered solely by 'Armstrong's Patent' (human muscle) the yard right next door might have had steam saws, and other powered equipment, since the middle of the nineteenth century.

The original study was very much of a local nature, since at that time most of the tools in Brixham Museum were of local provenance, but this no longer obtains and wider studies were needed. From this basis the book has grown, encompassing as many as possible of those trades which ministered to the vast fleets of sailing shipping of all descriptions, which once flourished in the world's oceans and waterways.

Collections of tools of the maritime trades are not so common as might be expected, in spite of our maritime history. They are not very well represented in the national museums, but more often turn up in the smaller local ones. It is only too easy to overlook these small but often very important groups of tools since they bear a direct relationship to their home district and its history, and are often regarded as nothing more than part of a folklife collection, which indeed they also are. In a way they represent a connecting link between local folklore and national history. Many tools remain in private hands, as treasured mementoes, parts of private tool collections, in use for other purposes or lying neglected and forgotten. Some have been brought to light by repeated

(*opposite*) A typical small shipyard at Plymouth, about 1900

11

appeals from interested museums such as that at Brixham or the East Anglian Maritime Museum at Great Yarmouth. But many more must still be about, neglected, rusting and rotting, unrecognised and apparently unwanted. Within a very short time memories of what they are, what they were used for, how they were used and who used them will be gone forever. At the time of writing there are still a few men living who used the more primitive tools, but their numbers are decreasing year by year.

Most of the tools described and illustrated here date from about 1800 onwards. Few tools, illustrations or adequate descriptions of earlier date exist. For many practical purposes the nineteenth century is the most useful, however, since it covered the period of most radical change. By 1800 the industrial revolution had started to make itself felt in some quarters of the shipbuilding industry, but not to any great degree. The blockmaking factories at Plymouth and Southampton, partly mechanised with water and horse power, and using an early form of mass production, were still under contract to the British Admiralty and their products were not available in sufficient quantity, outside the Admiralty, to affect the hand block-makers of the time. This was to come when Marc Brunel's true mass-production machinery was installed at the Naval Dockyards at Portsmouth and, although never used, Chatham allowed the Admiralty to produce all the blocks needed by the navy in the one dockyard. Then the blocks made by the Taylors of Southampton and de Dunstanville at Plymouth flooded onto the British market. By the end of the first quarter of the nineteenth century the block maker's trade depended more upon spar and pump making, and the various special sizes and types of block which the large block mills could not produce, than the smaller sizes in general use. Nevertheless, in some places it was more economic to produce all sizes of blocks almost to the end of the century. Even so, few of the tools used expressly for hand block-making have come down to us, due to the great reduction in the trade, and our knowledge of the trade itself is equally diminished.

Horse and water power were used in the larger sawmills before the end of the eighteenth century and steam came in during the early part of the nineteenth century. By 1850 many of the smaller shipyards were equipped with steam saws, but they were by no means universal. For much of the nineteenth century the circular saw was still really experimental, although it was originally invented some time in the second half of the eighteenth century. It is sometimes attributed to Marc Brunel, but I believe it was used in Taylor's blockmills at Southampton long before Brunel's time. Most of the early power saws were reciprocating types based on the handsaw action, and many of these remained in use well into the twentieth century until ousted by the large sizes of log bandsaws used today.

As the century reached its close new ideas on power tools came into being. This move was closely associated with the growth of first iron and then steel shipbuilding, and with the need for power tools for caulking, riveting, plate bending and so on. Overhead line shafting with belt drives to individual machines was powered first by steam, then by gas engines, and in a few places electric power was introduced soon after 1900. The first really portable power tools were driven by compressed air which was, and still is, conveyed from a central compressor plant through a fixed steel air line to fixed points throughout the yard. From the air line rubber and canvas hoses tap off the air to the various hand-held tools. Later in the twentieth century these were joined by the hand-held electric tool, and today they supplement each other. Until the full acceptance of these small power tools—and this depended upon the availability of power—the hand methods of previous centuries persisted, modified by the use of certain powered machinery such as saws and drilling machines.

World War II brought about the most radical changes, and the resulting impetus has affected even the smallest yards, continuing to do so today. During that period of strife some of the most unexpected tools appeared and were pressed into service. Only skilled men could have bored out the sterntube housings for a wooden minesweeper on the slipway using a cumbersome set of pump augers dating from about 1860—yet this was done, in World War II, at Brixham, when no other tools were available. Needless to say, the sterntube bedded perfectly. At the same time, the stimulus given by the efforts called for and made during World War II meant radical changes. Old, run-down and rather decrepit yards were given a new lease of life, finding themselves very much in demand. Government resources re-equipped many of the old yards in a manner which few could have afforded on their own. At the end of the war there were shipyards of many sizes all round Britain so equipped as to be able to compete with most of the larger establishments when it came to small craft construction. But at that time the demand was for larger vessels. By the time restrictions were eased on the supply of materials for vessels other than merchant craft, many small yards had gone out of business, or turned their hands to more lucrative trades then

13

in demand. The rise of small craft built of glass-reinforced plastic had not then begun; if it had, then no doubt many more small yards would still be in business today. In spite of all these changes, it is still possible to find small boatbuilders flourishing, usually in out-of-the-way places, whose only concession to modern boatbuilding techniques is a handful of electric tools and electric lighting in the boatshed.

I must make it clear that this is a first attempt at collating as much as possible about the tools and the way they were used, and without question much has been missed or overlooked. It is not an exhaustive study, and I hope that it may be the means of bringing to light much more material. What I present here is a collation of recorded evidence, verbal tradition, craftsmen's memories, my own memories of almost twenty years in a small shipyard working in both steel and wood, and information gleaned from tool collections in museums and private hands. The tools, their names and their uses as included here are those which I am satisfied were so called and so used. There were so many variations of tool, name, use and method throughout Britain that I am bound to have missed some points. There is a natural bias towards the West Country, not only because I happen to live and work there, but because it remained one of the strongholds of traditional shipbuilding methods longer than perhaps anywhere else in the British Isles. It was for this reason that Devon yards were chosen for the construction of the replica sailing vessels—*Mayflower II*, built at Brixham in 1957; *Nonsuch*, built at Appledore in 1970; and *Golden Hinde*, built at Appledore in 1973. Here the use of old tools has survived to some extent, though not to such a standard as might have been expected. Although the tools and methods used in the construction of these vessels were not all strictly traditional, and power tools were used, nevertheless the techniques used were very much in keeping with the original periods. Some of the techniques and skills were such that they are no longer called for in the normal work of the shipyards involved, and elderly retired craftsmen were called in to advise and sometimes to carry out the work itself. The natural pride which goes with fine crafts-manship was apparent in every move these men made, and shows in the finished work.

When compiling the material for the book, one of the things which impressed me most was the tremendous amount of effort involved in building a ship by the old methods. There must have been hours of back-breaking work with adzes and augers, and on the sawpit using pitsaws and ribsaws. I feel quite inadequate to describe the labours of those stout and incredibly skilled men, few of whom were literate, using little more than their own muscles and a few simple levers to work on pieces of timber which often needed several men to turn them over. I shudder at the thought of boring holes for deadwood bolts through some six to eight feet, maybe more, of oak, often enough wet and green at that, then driving the bolt, a bar of copper about one eighth of an inch oversize on the diameter, through the whole depth of the deadwood *without burring over the ends or bending the bar*, then riveting it into place. This was done five or six times at the after end of the keel, and again at the fore end, on each and every vessel. The effort, the sweat, the strain, the sheer brute force, tempered by the skill needed to avoid spoiling the whole bar of copper, is almost unbelievable. Yet it was almost an everyday task, only one of the many operations involved in the construction of each and every wooden ship. Small wonder that men followed the careers of their finest ships with a fervour bordering on adoration.

In some of the smaller yards this feeling still exists, born of a pride in workmanship which still pervades those industries which mass production has been unable to conquer. This pride was an important feature in the psychological make-up of the craftsman, regardless of his trade, and perhaps helped to compensate him for the disadvantages of working under a system which was purest tyranny in many cases. In spite of the most appalling abuses dissatisfaction with working conditions was seldom expressed; if it was, it was immediately suppressed. Only sixty-five years ago it was not unusual for a pair of sawyers to work on a sawpit from 6am to 6pm Monday to Friday, and from 6am to 4pm on Saturday, cutting timber for a single ship for weeks on end, for wages averaging twenty-one shillings (£1.05).

Conditions were so different from those of today, that one might say that the men themselves were different. Life was extremely hard for the working classes, a precarious, badly paid existence, and yet many men who were practically illiterate were able to produce masterful work, and many were able to finance their own businesses or even to own ships on the side. They belonged to an age that many of us find hard to comprehend, and we shall not see their like again. The smell of sawn timber and tarred rope, so familiar to those of us who have worked in shipyards building wooden ships, is a very nostalgic scent, and it is too easy to wax romantic. But nostalgia only sees what it wants to see, the best times, the better parts, and pushes the darker times into the background. Memories often play the same trick and it is frequently the best things which are recalled, though if pressed some men will tell pathetic stories of struggle—stories of their own children carrying buckets of water from the communal tap up long flights of steps to earn a crust of bread for breakfast from some of the more prosperous families, or of father's lunch consisting of a can of cold tea, about half a pint, which he could warm up at work, and two fairly thick slices of bread. This would have to last him from 6am until he left work at 6pm. Then again we might hear of the yards being short of work, men laid off, and crowds of them walking anything up to sixty miles to a place which had plenty of work, with their tools on their backs.

To blazes with the nostalgia. Let these tools speak out for themselves. Let the sweat grimed into their hafts talk of the really hard graft of living and working in such times, of toil the like of which most of us will never know. As you sit in your chair reading this, spare a thought for the men huddled over a fire of coal found in the mud under the coal staithes, or of scrap ends from the sawpits, who, half starved and overworked, helped Britain to put you where you are. Nay, they *were* the Britain that put you there.

1

EARLY TOOLS

The story of the evolution of tools is a long and complex one that is never really likely to be fully known, studded as it is with possibilities, probabilities, cross-fertilisation of ideas, parallel developments, independent inventions, cultures out of alignment and a multitude of other factors. Nevertheless I feel justified in including some of the tools used by man to build ships and boats in early days. Man as an animal is often distinguished from the lesser beasts by the fact that he alone discovered how to make and use a variety of tools. This is generally true. It took a long time to develop a more extensive range of tools, however, and it appears that even in Roman times the craftsmen were still basically either woodworkers or metalworkers (smiths) rather than carpenters, joiners, shipwrights and so on. Just when the trades became defined is not at all clear. Certain tradesmen were certainly recognised in Greek and Roman times, but only on a small scale. Odysseus was capable of building himself a rather sophisticated raft, and was able to use a variety of tools, yet his early training was that of a herdsman.

It seems logical to assume that as tools developed in their early stages their use was an accomplishment to which every man aspired. The range of tools in any one tribal sphere was not so great that mastery of every one was any vast achievement. All the same, a fair degree of skill was needed to be able to handle successfully a stone axe lashed to a wooden haft, which was a crank tool by any standards.

By the Middle Ages trades had become more clearly defined, with trade guilds for many crafts. Some form of apprenticeship was in use for training would-be craftsmen, though in England it was not until the reign of Elizabeth I that the Statute of Apprentices formulated for the first time some kind of legal standing for the system. Up to that time each of the trade guilds had its own methods and practices. The statute is generally accepted as an attempt to bring the guilds into line and regulate their practices rather than the introduction of new and revolutionary ideas. The trades involved were specified, and in fact the scope of the statute was very limited. Several additions were made to the original Act in succeeding reigns; one, during the reign of Queen Anne, brought in the trade of shipwright as one of those enumerated.

The Statute of Apprentices was not the great boon it might have been expected to be. In its original form it did not distinguish between a carpenter and a shipwright as individual crafts, yet weavers were either weavers of silk or of wool. In some cases the affinities of trades were recognised, in others the crafts were divided very rigidly, so that the wool weaver, for example, could not turn his hand to any other form of weaving when trade was slack, nor could the silk weaver. This led to much hardship in certain trades from time to time, and held back the economic growth of England to a considerable degree. But it did regularise the apprenticeship system, and also laid down the length of terms of service.

The actual separation of the trade of shipwright from that of carpenter seems to have taken place before this, first as ship's carpenter, though that trade is still recognised in many places today. In 1352 William de Asshendenne of Dartmouth, Devon, was appointed to select eighteen of the best 'carpenters for ships' to be found along the south coast of England and to place them in the king's service. It is uncertain whether this means shipwrights or ship's carpenters. The work they were to do was the converting of merchant ships into fighting ships, which at that time meant the addition of wooden fighting towers or castles fore and aft. Today's ship's carpenter might very well claim this as his work, rather than that of the shipwright. By 1500 it is clear that the trade of shipwright was being carried out under that name. It may have only been applicable to those men who built the hulls of ships and laid the decks, while the ship's carpenter did most, if not all, of the non-structural work.

When Henry V ordered his great ships to be built, one of these was built at Southampton, the *Grace de Dieu*. This was in 1418, and the man in charge of construction was Huggekyns, described as Master Carpenter of the king's ships. Henry VIII in the preface to a statute of 1540 included the trades of 'smythes, ropers, shipwrittes', which implies that the shipwright was then recognised as such. Charnock in his *History of Marine Architecture* refers to 'all the wrights of Scotland' in connection with the building of the *Great Michael* in Scotland in 1506. It was

Henry VIII who took steps to improve the standards of English ship-wrightry, setting up naval dockyards and importing the best foreign shipwrights and ship designers he could find or persuade to come, particularly from Genoa and Venice. Although these men were brought in to work on the improvement of English naval construction in the new Royal Dockyards, the effect was far-reaching. Design improved considerably, though that of contemporary French naval architects was still considered superior, but shipwrightry itself was improved beyond measure, both in the dockyards and in the smaller shipyards.

By the time the seventeenth century opened the craft of shipwrightry in England had evolved sufficiently away from normal carpentry to be possessed of those craft 'mysteries' which were so jealously guarded by the trades and guilds. Yet the trade had little standing in the eyes of most people. The Worshipful Company of Shipwrights was granted its first charter by James I in 1605, but in spite of this the general run of shipwrightry throughout the country was not highly regarded. Several attempts were made by members of the trade to raise it to a better standard of recognition, since it was for long regarded as the trade to put one's more worthless sons to. William Sutherland, in his collection of essays under the title of *The Shipbuilder's Assistant* (1711), wrote :

> . . . the proper business of a Shipwright is counted a very vulgar Imploy; and which a Man of very indifferent Qualifications may be Master of. Many have as mean an Opinion of it as a certain Gentleman, who told one of our former Master Builders, that he had a Blockhead of a Son uncapable to attain any other trade unless that of a Ship-carpenter, for which he designed him.

As well as recording the common attitude of the people towards the trade, Sutherland here suggests that the terms 'shipwright' and 'ship carpenter' were still virtually interchangeable.

The various treatises and papers published in the effort to raise the prestige of the trade revealed to a great extent the so-called 'mysteries' of the craft, and it is through them that we know so much of the work of some of England's leading master shipwrights such as Anthony Deane, the Petts and Matthew Baker. Some remain anonymous, though their writings have survived. But these works tell little, if anything, of the tools employed. All assumed that the types and uses of the various tools were known and understood, and wrote for shipwrights seeking to improve their understanding of design and those who, although unlikely to handle tools themselves, were keenly interested in the development and improvement of design.

It is apparent that the shipwright used many tools which were common to practically all other woodworking trades. In the distant past all these trades had a common origin, where woodworking tools were for woodworking, regardless of the specific type of woodwork involved. As specialisation came into being, so specialist adaptations of tools came into existence, and eventually special tools themselves were evolved to meet the specialist craftsman's needs in addition to the basic tools of any woodworker.

The complex curves of comparatively massive wooden structures such as are found in wood shipbuilding do not appear in any other trade. Therefore the tools used would be those most suited to shaping and working large shapes of highly individual outline from timber of very heavy scantlings. Frequently the shapes had to be cut straight from the log, which could be of tremendous size. Only hand tools were available. The saw was not always the best way to cut the log, and so it was that some of the largest axes in the world came into being for 'blocking out', as this operation was known. Wasteful in timber, perhaps, but sawn timber is not always suited to ship work, where the natural grown strength of the tree is a great asset. With such heavy sizes the wastage was often not so great as might have been expected, for the trees were carefully selected.

So from the ancient range of tools the axe and the adze were obvious choices, adapted to their special tasks. The adze is the particular tool of the shipwright's trade, and no other could be so adaptable for working the curves and shapes. The hammer, too, in a range of types seldom known as hammers, but certainly belonging to the same family of tools, was adopted. These three, and the saw, remained the basic shipwrights' tools, as indeed they still are in some parts of the world. Perhaps one should add an auger with which to make holes.

The briefest survey of simple shipbuilding methods shows how successful work can be carried out with only a few tools. Trees were felled and trimmed with the axe. The hammer drove wedges to split or rive the timber into planks, which were then cleaned up with the adze. The adze was used to smooth and shape the curves, the axe to shape the treenails or wooden pins to hold the ship together, the auger to bore the holes and the hammer to drive the treenails. The other necessity was skill in the use of these tools, and a knowledge of how a boat or ship should be built.

In early times the shipwright was not concerned with the conservation of timber, having plenty of trees to pick from. With ample supplies, economy of cutting was not important, and the shipwright would be more likely to economise on his own labour, where possible. To some extent this would be reflected in his choice of trees. Curved branches made strong curved frames, straight trees made the best long planks. That may be an over-simplified explanation of how a ship might be built, but it serves to illustrate that much could be done with a very small tool chest.

The earliest tools that have survived are those imperishable ones of stone, the familiar Stone Age axes and adzes. Any contemporary wooden tools there may have been have either not survived or their remains have not yet been found or recognised as such. Nevertheless, some early methods of hafting are known from remains preserved in peat bogs. Such things as the wooden shanks of drills, if these existed, have not so far been found; neither does it appear that the cutting tips have, though some microliths could easily have served this purpose. This may be a matter of non-recognition due to the lack of wooden shafts.

Figure 1 shows a few of the many stone tools that have been found. Figure 1(a), from an example in the Zurich Landesmuseum, shows a small stone axe head fitted to a haft which appears to be little more than a slightly modified club. It is set through a hole cut in the haft, and possibly in the original state a lashing helped to prevent the haft splitting. Figure 1(b) is from a peat bog, and has been reconstructed by Danish archaeologists. Again the head is set in a socket through the head of the haft, and the thickening of the haft at this point suggests that troubles had been experienced here. This must have been a major point of weakness with stone tools, and one which could not easily be solved until the advent of metal. Even so, these reconstructions using the original stone axe heads have been successfully used to fell trees in very little more time than that taken with a modern steel axe head. Figure 1(c) shows an adze with the method of hafting found on northern European examples. This was by no means the only way of attaching the head to a haft, though it can not have been a very easy task. The adze is designed to cut across grain and down grain with a slicing action. The across-grain action is a sideways movement, not across into the grain as with an axe, and consequently the adze on its own cannot cut down a tree above an inch or two in diameter. But used between two suitably placed axe kerfs

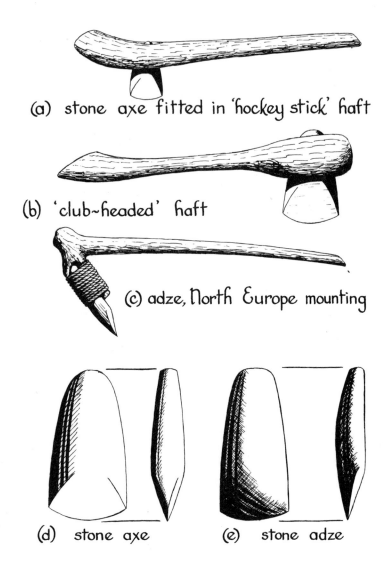

(a) stone axe fitted in 'hockey stick' haft

(b) 'club-headed' haft

(c) adze, North Europe mounting

(d) stone axe   (e) stone adze

Figure 1   Neolithic tools

to clear wood and make a wider single kerf, cutting across the tree from one side to the other it can be a great aid in felling. This wide kerf is deepened with the axe, and again the adze used to clear the area between the two axe marks, making it possible to speed up the felling of a large tree. Figures 1(d) and (e) show the essential difference between the two tools. It has been suggested that in the later Bronze Age some of the socketed axes or celts could be turned at right-angles and used as adzes, but this is hardly likely, as the angle or set of the cutting edges is totally different. I must admit that I have never seen anything like the adze form in bronze, but since stone tools continued to be used throughout the period this is not conclusive. The smooth curving cutting stroke obtainable with the stone adze heads, primitive though they may have been, would certainly not be provided by the bronze celt, which had its cutting edge in line with the centre line of the casting.

Stone tools are not necessarily thousands of years old. In many parts of the world they were used until quite recently, and in a few places still are. Fortunately from time to time someone appears who faithfully records what he sees and hears. Shortly after 1800 one such man, an official of the British administration in New Zealand, watched the Maoris building their great wooden canoes, and recorded for posterity the methods and tools used in what was essentially a Stone Age society, albeit an artistically sophisticated one. Their tools were like those of the Neolithic period, finely polished to produce a straight and purposeful cutting edge, not the crude flaked tools of the Palaeolithic. Once this stage had been reached, craftsmanship followed naturally. The Maori tools were of a hard black glassy type of rock, possibly obsidian, with very keen polished cutting edges. Their method of hafting adzes was slightly different from that found in northern Europe, as Figure 2(a) shows.

The raw material for the canoe was the huge kauri pine, the usable part of the trunk being perhaps eighty feet or more long and some eight feet thick, giving a girth of about twenty-five feet. The trees were felled by one of two methods, one being that already outlined using axe and adze. Two parallel cuts were made with the axe, then the 'land' between was cleared with the adze. The groove was then deepened and again the land was cleared. This was repeated until sufficient had been removed to direct the fall of the tree, then work started on the opposite side of the trunk. The other method of felling, which was used more rarely, employed the ram chisel, Figure 2(b), which resembled a large Palaeo-

23

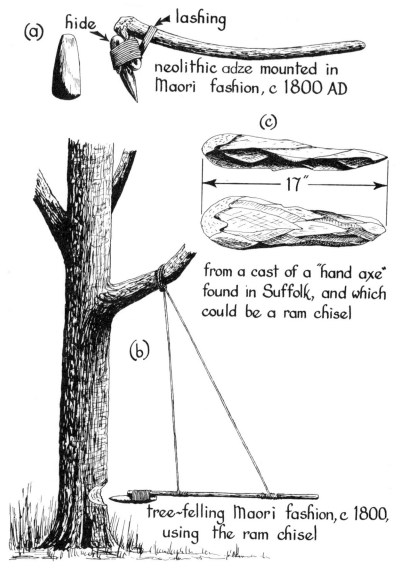

(a) hide ← lashing

neolithic adze mounted in Maori fashion, c 1800 AD

(c)

17"

from a cast of a "hand axe" found in Suffolk, and which could be a ram chisel

(b)

tree-felling Maori fashion, c 1800, using the ram chisel

Figure 2   Early tools

lithic hand axe. It was one of the few tools the Maoris did not bother to polish, and was left in the rough chipped state. This large stone was lashed to a stout pole or beam which was suspended from a branch of the tree to be felled. Several men then swung the chisel against the trunk of the tree. From the enormous size of a plaster cast I have seen and handled made from a so-called hand axe of the Palaeolithic period found in Suffolk, it is possible that this method was used in parts of Britain. The sheer size and weight of the stone original, Figure 2(c), must surely count against its use as a hand axe.

Having felled their chosen tree the Maoris trimmed the trunk with axes, sometimes using fire to help them. One old native is recorded as saying that they used two adzes, one of stone, the other of fire, to shape the hull. The tree was laid down with its natural shake horizontal, and the top half adzed and burnt down level. The use of heated stones in this and the next stage, hollowing out the hull, seems logical in preference to what might be termed 'bare' fire, hence perhaps the native analogy with the stone adze. While the inside was being carved away, the final work being done by highly skilled men using adzes only, the outside was also being roughed out. This, too, was finally finished with great skill, often being entirely covered with small neat adze patterns. Sanding down, when needed, was done with a block of sandstone. One strake of planking was added on each side of the dugout hull, and when possible this consisted of a single plank on each side which might be more than sixty feet long and fifteen inches wide at the centre. These were cut out of a whole tree, probably riven and adze-finished. The planks were drilled along one edge with holes to match in the topsides of the hull, then sewn on. The stitches were strained tight using a Y-shaped branch, the two arms serving as levers to tighten the cord wound round the butt as it was rolled along the gunwale. Pegs were driven from inside the hull to secure the cord. Details of the drill do not seem to have been recorded. It could have been a bow drill tipped with obsidian, or perhaps fire was used. The joint between the plank and the topside of the dugout hull was covered with a convex strip of wood inside and out, the stitches passing over these strips on each side. Presumably this was to prevent chafe against the square edges of the holes in the planks and hull. The canoe was completed with a stem post and a stern post, probably put in before the planking was sewn on. These uprights were elaborately carved, and additional decoration was added to the bulwark strake. Despite the primitive tools, the carvings of these canoes, as on the Maori houses,

25

were true masterpieces. Cross beams which served as rowing or paddling thwarts were lashed to the bulwark planks, and the entire bottom was finished off with a grating made of small timbers lashed together.

The procedure of building a Maori canoe was carried out to a strict ritual, perhaps with more of a religious flavour than one is accustomed to in modern shipbuilding. Yet ritual is still with us in many ways. Apart from the annual Mayday ceremonies, the playing of certain rather curious games in various parishes on particular days of the year, and so on, there is still often the keel laying ceremony, and the breaking of a bottle of champagne over the bows of the latest supertanker at her launching. These are the remnants of rituals which go back thousands of years. In Greek classical times it was customary to pour a libation of wine into the sea at the launching of a vessel or even the start of a voyage to placate Poseidon, god of the oceans. But the origin must be much further back. Then, too, there are the tricks played on the new apprentice, and the traditional ceremony at the completion of an apprenticeship. All go back to the times when few could read or write, and the necessity of impressing a particular point called for something that would be remembered.

Ritual has played an important rôle in the development of many crafts. It was basically a means of impressing upon a simple people the correct way of doing things, and ensuring that they were done in the correct order and the correct way. Written instructions were of no use in a society in which reading and writing did not exist. So the elders of the tribes evolved the ritual, mingling it with religious ceremonial to impress it on the minds of their people. Even though each task might be a relatively simple one, it must be carried out properly and in the correct order. Dire consequences were threatened if things were not done properly. The long and complicated ceremonies might go on for weeks on end, but the ritual almost certainly ensured a satisfactory conclusion. And so it went on, generation after generation, passing on the knowledge from father to son throughout the tribe. Eventually it became more a religious ritual than the straightforward building of a canoe, but it served its purpose. In the more progressive tribes the elders gradually added the latest ideas to improve their craft, but the air of mystery and magic was retained.

As time went by and changes came, the written word took over to a certain degree, though by the serving of an apprenticeship it was still possible to learn a trade without being able to read and write. Ritual still pervades many of the really old trades today, though the original purpose has long since been forgotten. Present-day shipbuilding terminology, too, is full of ancient relics, many of the words going back to the misty past; the planking or plating of a ship is still referred to as the 'skin', and the term 'frame', too, must surely go back to the days of boats of wicker and skin, forerunners of the coracle and curragh. 'Stem' may come from the name given to a tree used on top of the great trunk from which the dugout was made, rather than the idea that it was this part of the vessel which 'stemmed' the tide.

As was seen in Figure 1, the hafting of tools in the Neolithic period still left much to be desired. A few tools have been found with bored holes for hafting, but they are relatively few compared with the undrilled patterns. The task of drilling a stone with the primitive tools available must have occupied many days, and the result was not satisfactory if the tool was to be used and not to serve merely as a badge of rank. The earlier bored stones are generally of softer material, in the form of hammers or maces. Often water-rounded pebbles were used, drilled through the thickest part. Figure 3(a) shows a typical example, made from a water-rounded pebble of oolitic limestone. The hole is tapered from each side, giving an hourglass shape, produced by drilling with a tapered point first from one side until the point broke surface, then turning the stone and drilling back into the drill hole. The exact method of drilling is not known, but an intelligent guess might be made that a simple bow drill was used, tipped with flint, and using flint dust or sharp sand as an abrasive. While it is true that many of the world's native tribes did not use the bow in any form, many did. It is problematical which came first, the fire drill, the bow drill for boring, or the hunting bow.

The use of metal for tools came in with the Bronze Age, although in Egypt there was a Copper Age which slightly preceded it. The admixture of tin to copper made a much harder material, and the life of tools of bronze was much longer than that of copper tools. Stone tools continued in use, and were still made and used side by side with both bronze and iron. It is significant that some highly finished stone hammers and axe-hammers appeared with parallel-sided bored holes, while few examples of bronze hammers are known. I personally cannot recall having ever located one. It seems possible that stone was still used for hammers and adzes during the Bronze Age. One of these stone axe-hammers is shown in Figure 3(b). Again no tools have survived to show how the hole was

(a)

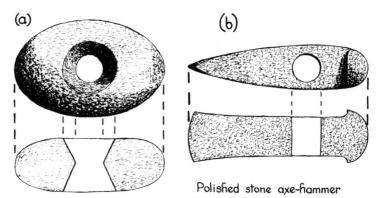

Stone hammer or macehead
with "hour-glass" hole drilled
from both sides, using a waterworn
pebble for base

(b)

Polished stone axe-hammer
with parallel-sided hole

(c)

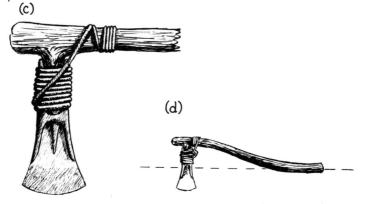

Mounting a palstave on
a haft, using a rawhide
lashing

(d)

Balancing an axe (or palstave)
by means of a cranked haft

Figure 3   Early tools

produced, but to do this without a hardened steel bit would call for a tubular bit of soft metal, used with flint dust or sharp sand. The modern lapidiary uses a similar method for the hardest of stones, and it should be noted that the example shown is made of a close-grained granite, quite a different proposition from the oolitic limestone of Figure 3(a). The difficulty of satisfactorily mounting the stone with the hourglass hole must be apparent, the parallel hole being a far better proposition. But these hammers are not very common, and it seems likely that some form of wooden mallet was used far more widely than the stone hammers.

The whole question of hafting tools is a very complicated one. For thousands of years stone heads were held to wooden hafts with thonging, a practice found the world over. Yet for tools of the axe, adze and hammer types this is most unsatisfactory. Even the drilling of holes for hafting was not the answer, and until the evolution of metal techniques there was very little choice. With metal, the desired shape could be cast, instead of laboriously chipping and polishing it from solid stone. But ideas do not always travel very fast. One would have thought that men who could drill parallel-sided holes in stones in the Bronze Age might have realised that a round hole or an oval one could very easily be cast in metal, but it did not follow. In fact, in northern Europe the whole theory of tool hafting worked itself into a veritable rut.

In Egypt metal tools, first of copper, later of bronze, developed more logically. Sir J. Gardner Wilkinson, writing in *A Popular Account of the Ancient Egyptians* (1854) stated that of the many tools found at Thebes, the blades were of bronze, the hafts acacia or tamarisk and the method of fastening was by hide thongs. Elsewhere in the same work he stated that the bronze axe heads were fastened with bronze pins and then bound in thongs. This is borne out by, and to some extent explains, some of the Egyptian pictures. They went on to develop hafting in the eastern Mediterranean in a manner similar to that used today, with a cast-in eye in line with the haft.

North of the Alps, Bronze Age Europe tried a variety of methods. Starting with the flat cast axe, Figure 4(a), lashed on to a flat on the side of a wooden haft, or into a slot in the end of it, side flanges were developed, Figure 4(c), that called for a haft with a stub on one side. Sometimes a rolled form of flange was produced, Figure 4(b), which partly encased the haft. From this the palstave, Figure 4(d), emerged, with a stop-ridge to try to prevent the haft from splitting. The method of hafting is shown in Figures 3(c) and (d). The balancing of a tool was

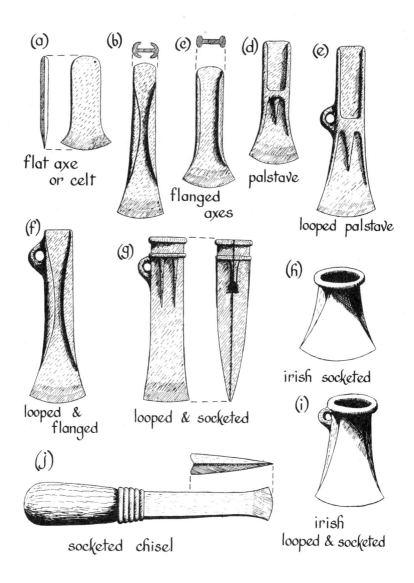

(a) flat axe or celt

(b) (c) flanged axes

(d) palstave

(e) looped palstave

(f) looped & flanged

(g) looped & socketed

(h) irish socketed

(i) irish looped & socketed

(j) socketed chisel

Figure 4   Bronze-Age tools

appreciated early on, and cranked hafts compensated for the imbalance of the head. This survives today in many tools, notably in the ship-wright's adze, with its double-bent haft. Figures 4(e) and (f) show the older forms of flanged axe and palstave now fitted with loops to aid lashing to the haft, and these were fairly closely followed by the fully socketed axe, Figure 4(g), also with lashing loops or eyes. Here the stub of the haft was completely housed inside the head of the axe. The two Irish examples, Figures 4(h) and (i), are basically the same but with the Irish characteristic of a shorter and relatively broader head. Figure 4(h) has a pronounced rim to aid lashing, a feature which is repeated on the looped version. All the types from Figure 4(b) onwards required the use of a haft with a side stub, and this, surely, was a major source of trouble. For some curious reason the Bronze Age smiths of northern Europe were obsessed with this idea, until the Iron Age brought in new ideas from abroad.

The development of socketed tools also led to the production of socketed chisels and gouges, and with tools such as these the craftsmen of the times were able to expand their trade vocabulary considerably. The chisel shown in Figure 4(j) was a serviceable tool, allowing for the fact that it was cast in bronze, a relatively soft metal. This and other examples show a collar decoration resembling thong lashings, which could be a residual from an earlier form, examples of which have not yet come to light.

A feature of all Bronze Age tools is the expanded cutting edge. Those tools which from time to time are found without this feature invariably turn out never to have been sharpened for use. Sharpening was done by softening the edge in the fire, then hammering it out. This consolidated and rehardened the soft metal. Experiments have shown that this pro-duced a fair cutting edge. Bronze Age chisels are seldom found in a range of sizes, but why bother when the chisel could be widened or narrowed at will?

Mention of tools in Egypt has already been made, and it must be agreed that there were no standardised types. Figures 5 I (a), (b) and (c) show three versions of the adze used by Egyptian shipwrights at various times. These had flat bronze blades lashed onto the outside of a curved haft, producing a balanced tool. Figure 5 I (d) is an iron adze from Abydos, of the type known during the nineteenth century as a slot adze, with an iron stirrup and wedge to hold the blade. A variety of hafts are shown in Figures 6(b), (c) and (e), the last being a short-hafted carpenter's

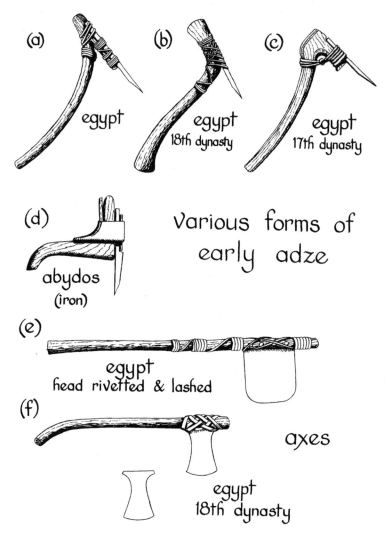

(a) egypt

(b) egypt 18th dynasty

(c) egypt 17th dynasty

(d) abydos (iron)

various forms of early adze

(e) egypt head rivetted & lashed

(f) egypt 18th dynasty

axes

Figure 5   I The Middle East

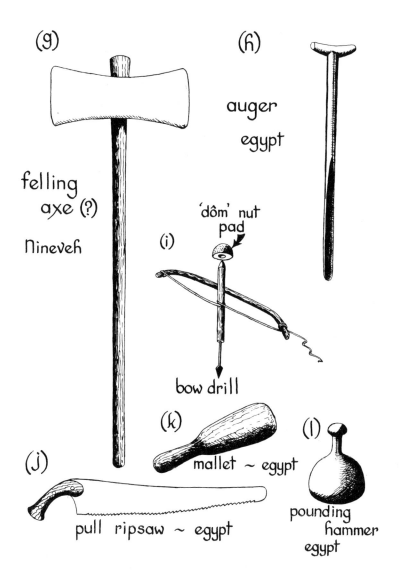

(g)

felling
axe (?)

Nineveh

(h)

auger

egypt

(i)

'dôm' nut
pad

bow drill

(j)

pull ripsaw ~ egypt

(k)

mallet ~ egypt

(l)

pounding
hammer
egypt

Figure 5   II The Middle East

version. The adzes shown are rather primitive, but this may be artistic distortion or simplification. Certainly some of the hafts look highly impractical and quite improbable. Figures 5 I (b) and (c) show that some attention was being paid to the shaping of the haft. The axe in Figure 5 I (e) is of the type described by Sir J. Gardner Wilkinson, riveted to the haft with bronze rivets and lashed with thongs. Figure 5 I (f) is another form which appears to have been slotted into one side of the haft without riveting, then lashed firmly with thongs. It must have been a rather unsteady arrangement. Figure 5 II (g) is of a large axe found at Nineveh, and described as a felling axe. Somehow I think it more suited to ceremonial or battle purposes, though it is easy to be wrong with these early tools. Figure 5 II (h) shows an iron hand auger from Egypt, and this represents a departure from the strap or bow drill. Its use is self-explanatory, and it could well be the ancestor of the hand augers found down the ages at almost all later periods. The bow drill still appeared for lighter drilling or boring jobs, as in Figure 5 II (i). In this instance the bit is of bronze, and the top pad is made from the 'dom' nut of the Theban palm. Figure 6(g) shows it in use, and Figure 6(f) shows another form of drill of which no example seems to have been recovered. It appears to have been operated by twirling the shank between the hands. Figure 5 II (j) shows the form of a bronze ripsaw, and its use is illustrated in Figure 6(d). The teeth are set the opposite way to those in a modern saw, and the saw was pulled and not pushed. This is logical for a saw made of a soft metal which if pushed would buckle at the first stroke. Again we have one of those strange idiosyncracies of tools. The form was dictated by the material. Yet in southern Europe steel saws of the same pull type continued to be made well into the nineteenth century. In the north of the continent the Viking saw was a small push tool. Figure 5 II (k) is a wooden mallet which is shown being used in Figure 6(b). This is the normal procedure for any woodworker using a chisel, striking it with a wooden mallet. Figure 5 II (l) shows another form of wooden mallet, used in a rather different style. The handle was held in the fist and it was used with a pounding action. Apart from these two wooden mallets I have not been able to find any other form of hammer among the Egyptian tools, and it is quite possible that no other form was used.

The illustrations in Figure 6 are all taken from Egyptian pictures, and they show how the conventions of the original artists distorted the figures and probably the tools as well. The two men wielding axes in Figure 6(c) in particular do not appear to be effective craftsmen.

(a) making a papyrus boat

(b) building a wooden boat

(c) 'blocking out' a log

(d) ripsawing

(e) carpenter's adze

(f) breast drill

(g) bow drill

Figure 6   Egypt

That the Greeks were great shipbuilders is known both from their history and from such works as *The Odyssey*, though on reading translations of this work it is almost impossible to ascribe it to any one cultural period. Tools are mentioned in it, as in the well-known passage concerning the putting out of the single eye of the Cyclops, Polyphemus :

> There lay by a sheepfold a . . . club of olive wood . . . I . . . cut off from it a portion as it were a fathom's length and set it down by my fellows and bade them fine it down . . . while I stood by and sharpened it to a point, and straightway I took it and hardened it in the bright fire . . . For their part they seized the bar of olive wood, that was sharpened to a point, and thrust it into his eye, while I from my place aloft turned it about, as when a man bores a ship's beam with a drill while his fellows below spin it with a strap, which they hold at either end, and the auger runs round continually.

and again, referring to the hideous noise the operation made :

> . . . and as when a smith dips an axe or adze in chill water with a great hissing, when he would temper it . . . for hereby anon comes the strength of the iron . . .

From this one might be forgiven for suspecting that the episode was placed in the Iron Age, with the reference to the use of and means of tempering iron, yet in Book V of *The Odyssey* we read that Calypso gave to Odysseus a great bronze axe, double-edged, hafted with olive wood, fastened well (an allusion to the difficulties experienced with hafting early tools). Next she gave him a polished adze. Here the story seems to fit the Bronze Age, both from the use of the bronze axe and the polished adze, which, from its description as 'polished', was most likely of polished stone rather than metal. Calypso also brought augers, though they are not described, and Odysseus built himself a 'raft', boring each piece and making all fast with treenails and dowels.

No doubt the original story or group of stories has been added to over the centuries between the first telling and the final committing to writing, and without doubt translation into modern English has not quite put over the original intent, as so often happens. There is even a difference between translations of the mid-nineteenth century and those of a century later. For our purposes perhaps the earlier ones are best, for the technology of the time was far closer to Greek methods and therefore far better understood than by modern translators. The Odyssey seems

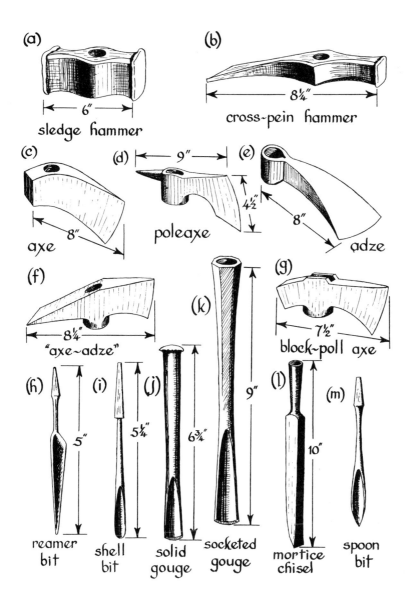

(a) sledge hammer — 6″

(b) cross-pein hammer — 8¼″

(c) axe — 8″

(d) poleaxe — 9″ / 4½″

(e) adze — 8″

(f) "axe~adze" — 8¼″

(g) block~poll axe — 7½″

(h) reamer bit — 5″

(i) shell bit — 5¼″

(j) solid gouge — 6¾″

(k) socketed gouge — 9″

(l) mortice chisel — 10″

(m) spoon bit

Figure 7 I Roman tools

to be a collection of folk stories dating back a very long way, parts being brought up to date, as it were, with the passing of each different cultural period.

As for the tools described in *The Odyssey*, the method of boring is an adaptation of the bow drill on a rather larger scale. The bow had been replaced by two men, one at each end of a strap working round the drill shank. I believe it has been observed in use in parts of China, but this is not first-hand information, and generally it fits in well with some of the older types of tool still used in the Mediterranean. Bronze axes of the type said to have been given to Odysseus by Calypso, and of such a high standard, have not yet come to light, but there is still a chance. The use of treenails and dowels is interesting, throwing a new slant on construction in that area, though of course it is not really dateable.

With the coming of iron it was possible to develop tools further. By Roman times there was a wide range for the discerning craftsman in wood to choose from. In some cases the tools developed by the time the Romans were entrenched in Britain have still not been improved upon, except perhaps in the quality of the material. Figure 7 shows a selection of Roman iron tools, many of which would not disgrace a modern tool chest. The sledge hammer, Figure 7 I (a) is so familiar as to need no comment, and probably the same applies to the cross-pein hammer, Figure 7 I (b). The axe in Figure 7 I (c) is slightly drop-nosed by modern styles, but equally as serviceable, and the poleaxe, Figure 7 I (d), is almost identical with those used in the nineteenth century. The adze in Figure 7 I (e) may be a mattock rather than an adze, but in common with the other tools it shows the fully developed haft socket. The so-called 'axe-adze' shown in Figure 7 I (f) is probably more of an agricultural implement than a craftsman's tool, but the heavy block-poll axe in Figure 7 I (g) looks a useful tool for working in the woodlands. Various drill bits, as in Figures 7 I (h), (i) and (m) make it clear that some form of brace was used, though again I know of no actual example. Presumably it was mainly of wood. Gouges and chisels are shown in Figures 7 I (j), (k) and (l). Socketed chisels and gouges were apparently the commonest, from the numbers that have been found, and the modern-looking mortice chisel has still not been bettered. Solid shanked chisels and gouges were also fairly common. The curious form of adze in Figure 7 II (n) is something of an exception to the general run of Roman tools. It has its head pinned and strapped on. Figures 7 II (o) and (p) are iron drawknives, which may or may not have once been fitted with wooden

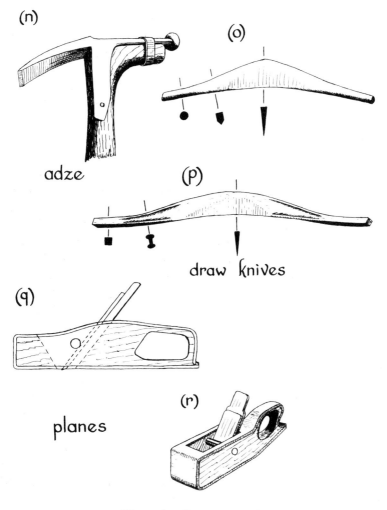

(n)

(o)

adze

(p)

draw knives

(q)

planes

(r)

Figure 7 II Roman tools

handles. The plane shown in Figures 7 II (q) and (r) appears to have been the invention of the Romans. Most Roman types had a metal frame, or at least a metal sole pinned right through the body. It is possible that the reconstructions here are not strictly correct, and the wedge should be above the single plane iron.

The hammers used by the Romans were sometimes faced with a small piece of steel to take the wear of continual use. This, according to one popular account of the Roman occupation of Britain published in the

1920s, was hailed as a great discovery, and it was suggested that this was one of those little tricks which had been lost. Yet this is precisely what the coachbuilder's blacksmiths in London were doing in the 1890s, and without doubt they were not the only ones. It is a great pity that, even today, there is quite a gulf between the archaeologist and the practices of the present and the recent past. Over-specialisation has its drawbacks.

Following the breakdown of the Roman period in Britain there followed the times known as the Dark Ages, when the prevailing influences were the Romans and a hangover from the British Iron Age. Then came the Saxons bringing their own tools with them. We do not have from the Saxon period the useful hoards of tools that the Romans left us, but this may be remedied in time. From those tools that have been found, and from illuminated manuscripts and the Bayeux Tapestry, I have drawn the selection shown in Figure 8. The first two, Figures 8(a) and (b), are the Saxon long axe in its two most usual forms. The second of these is nearly always found as a side axe, but both seem to have been dual-purpose implements, for use as tools or weapons, and are found illustrated as battle axes. The curved top shown in Figure 8(b) would be an advantage for side cutting without detracting from its use as a weapon of war. The so-called 'short' long axe is shown in Figure 8(c), and this seems a logical development of the long axe, in which the small size of the socket must have been a distinct disadvantage. Shortening the head would reduce the strain on the socket and make for a more stable tool. Figure 8(c) is found in both normal and side-cutting versions. The more practical style of axe is found in Figure 8(d), with its side-cutting version in Figure 8(g). In these two, the socket has developed more naturally as a part of the head. The strap adze, Figure 8(e), is not so far removed from the nineteenth-century version, but the common adze, Figure 8(f), if this is the correct identification, suffered from the same weaknesses as the long axe. I remain to be convinced that this is not a form of mattock or hoe. In spite of their great prowess as seamen (as witness the Roman fear of the Saxon pirates) they were basically a nation of farmers. It seems likely that the shaping of their tools was influenced by agricultural needs rather than those of the craftsman.

The drill stock in Figure 8(h) is drawn from a very indistinct passage of the Bayeux Tapestry, and seems to have been a two-handed version of the later brace or wimble stock. The auger, Figure 8(i), was presumably made to fit into a wooden handle, not as a bit for the drill stock. This spoon form of auger lasted well into the nineteenth century.

40

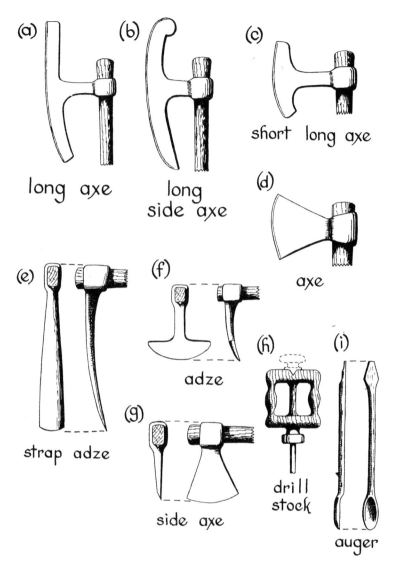

(a) long axe

(b) long side axe

(c) short long axe

(d) axe

(e) strap adze

(f) adze

(g) side axe

(h) drill stock

(i) auger

Figure 8   Saxon tools

On the whole Viking tools seem to have been better formed and made than those of the Saxons, but there were affinities. I have long been of the opinion that the Viking ship was an offshoot or development from the older Saxon ship, rather than a distinctly separate trend, and the similarity of their tools would therefore be rather expected. The better

41

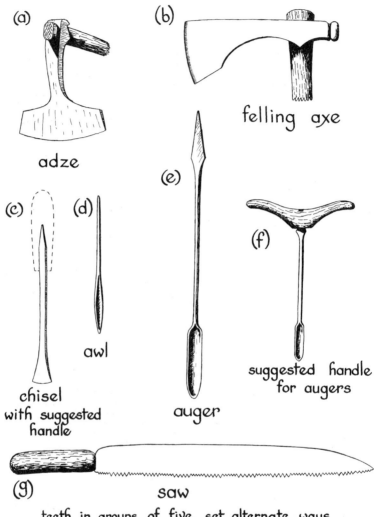

(a)

(b)

felling axe

adze

(e)

(c)   (d)

(f)

awl

chisel
with suggested
handle

auger

suggested handle
for augers

(g)   saw
teeth in groups of five, set alternate ways

Figure 9   Viking tools

quality of Viking tool-making is to be expected, too, from a race who
valued craftsmanship. The Viking felling axe, Figure 9(b), although
with a rather short socket, is well formed and practical. The same style
can be found in paintings made in Europe throughout the Middle Ages.
The adze, Figure 9(a), is very close to the Saxon model, though more
robust, not so sharply curved on the cutting edge and again with a

better formed socket. But it is not quite of the quality one would expect from such fine shipbuilders, and it is likely that the true Viking ship-building adze has yet to come to light. The chisel in Figure 9(c) appears to have been fitted into a handle in the conventional way, with a tang, but it also shows the fantail typical of the Bronze Age. This again may have been partly due to the method of sharpening, though this is an iron tool; perhaps it is merely a design legacy from earlier times. The awl in Figure 9(d) must also have had a simple wooden handle. The spoon auger, Figure 9(e), is of quite modern appearance, and the handle that I have suggested is based on a number which appear in paintings of the Middle Ages. The Viking saw, Figure 9(g), looks more like a modern breadknife than a saw. The teeth have no rake, so that it could cut both ways, and they are set in groups of five to either side. For a shipwright's saw it is far too small, except for fine work, and the general opinion seems to be that larger timbers were riven and axed or adzed to a finish. This saw was of iron, and it might well have been used pulled towards the user, but the handle suggests that this was not the case.

This review of some of the tools of earlier times is by no means exhaustive, being intended to throw into perspective the tools which follow. No doubt there were many tools used which are never likely to be found. It is hard to imagine that some of the work which was so well carried out was done with such a small range of tools, but it could have been the case. I have probably missed out many tools completely, but at this stage this is not very important. The sandstone blocks used by the Maoris are not the kind of things to attract the attention as shipwrights' tools, yet something like them must have been used wherever wood-working was carried on. They have been found, but in nothing like the numbers we might expect. The ancient shipwright, in common with his modern counterpart, might well have disposed of his worn-out tools in the age-old way—with a hefty heave into the water—unless the iron was salvable. The mud of our rivers, near shipyard sites of any period, must be thick with discarded tools and 'mistakes' disposed of on the quiet.

There is always the problem of recognition and identification of tools and implements on early sites, and it is difficult to know just how this should be dealt with. Techniques also evolve, as well as tools, leading to the discarding of certain special tools in favour of different ones more suited to the new methods. Thus the older tools lie in a corner forgotten, until they either rot away or are cleared out, their purpose lost with the passing of the men who used them.

2

WORKSHOPS AND PREMISES

In the beginning boats were probably built on the most convenient piece of land adjacent to both a source of materials and the water. In many respects this still applies, though with modern transport and the development of glassfibre reinforced plastic hulls it is not so essential. Today boats are built in Birmingham and places similarly distant from the sea, but with the source of materials close at hand. For relatively small craft this is no disadvantage, as road haulage can be arranged to all parts of the country. Transport developments have changed many things. Until the coming of the railways and the application of the internal combustion engine to heavy haulage, larger items had to be manhandled and horse-carted at low speeds over tough terrain, or sent by sea.

Until quite late in the nineteenth century it was possible for men to build ships for themselves almost wherever the shore or coast was suitable. Not many carried out this scheme, but it was known in a number of places in the West Country, particularly Devon and Cornwall, and some instances are rumoured from Scotland. The prospective owner-builder selected his site and rented or leased it for a short term. Then he hired a shipwright and a pair of sawyers. Often the shipwright was one of the sawyers. These men set to digging a sawpit on the site. The design of the hull was generally left to the shipwright, based on a brief from the owner, and probably settled between them by the use of a half-model carved on traditional and well-tried lines to meet the owner's needs. Timber was selected from the stocks of a local timber merchant, and carted or perhaps rafted to the site, then sawn out on the sawpit. Temporary keel blocks would be laid, and the keel laid. As building went ahead staging, perhaps made from offcuts from the pitsaw or from 'small stuff'—about four to six inches thick, seldom straight, and with the bark still on—would rise around the hull. A stout branch on a convenient tree might well be fitted up as a hoist with blocks and tackle for lifting heavy timbers, and rollers, levers and wedges were widely used. Usually the selected sites for this kind of work were practically inaccessible by road or track, only a footpath or cliff path leading to them, and materials had to be brought in by water. At times deserted former shipyard sites were used, but most of these were in demand for the regular shipwrights. Long before the vessel was ready for launching other craftsmen would be called in. The block and spar maker, if the shipwright was not to do this as well, would take measurements from the model and compute his spar sizes. He would set up his trestles or horses on the site and start shaping the mast and spars. The rigger would come, consult with 'Blocky', and work out the rigging, sketching it roughly on a scrap of paper or the short end of a plank. The rigger often worked in his own loft, cutting splicing and serving the rigging as needed. The final details were worked out on the site, on the actual vessel. The sailmaker would be called in, and he, in consultation with the rigger and the block and spar maker, would decide how to cut the sails. The sailmaker also worked in a loft, and often a rigger and a sail-maker shared the same loft. Much of their work was done together, and in the final stages of rigging and fitting sails they co-operated. The various craftsmen called in might each have a mate or an apprentice, and the owner would help with much of the work himself. Being normally a seafarer, his own knowledge of many of the things needed would make him of use to most trades, and he would be kept pretty busy. But all told there would seldom be above a dozen men involved in the whole construction. When the vessel had been launched the site would be roughly cleaned up. If the land was used for grazing then the sawpit might be filled in, but more likely it was left for the next customer. In some cases these sites proved so useful that new shipyards sprang up, in others the sites are quite forgotten, and they are not easy to find today.

By far the greater number of ships were built in the more conventional shipyards, and many small undertakings were sited round the British coastline and on the banks of rivers. Some consisted of only one slipway and perhaps one or two sheds. Others had a number of building slips and a range of sheds for the various trades. Some ports started off with a series of one-slip yards next door to each other which eventually amalgamated into one larger shipyard. These yards were very simple, and slipways were squeezed in wherever there was suitable access to the water with room for a sawpit, for the slip (which might be sideways on to the water), and room to lay off the lines. Shelter might almost have been thought a luxury in some of the smaller places. A building slip consisted of a reasonably smooth run of land or hard beach upon which a series of heavy keel blocks were laid. Heavy timbers driven vertically into the ground secured the lowest blocks, the grounds, which were dogged firmly together. The keel blocks were dogged down on top of the grounds, their top faces lined up by packing slips inserted between the grounds and the keel blocks. The side-launching technique was used where the land was too narrow or too steep for a conventional slipway. Although hailed during World War II as a startling innovation, side launching was practised in England from at least the eighteenth century. In such cases the keel blocks were laid down parallel to the river bank. In either case launchways were temporary, laid down only when needed. They consisted of two main components, the groundways and the sliding ways. Groundways were laid down and secured firmly, extending from beneath the vessel to at least low water mark. The sliding ways were only about the length of the vessel, if it was a small one, or of each of the launching cradles. They were laid to slide along the length of the groundways, with a lip to guide them along one side. The cradles were built up on the sliding ways supporting the hull at either end. The weight of the ship was gradually transferred from the building shores to the cradles, until it stood clear of the keel blocks and rested in the cradles. The weight was now taken solely by the launchway. Iron dogs were used for all fastenings in building the cradles, though in some yards prefabricated sections of cradles were kept ready bolted together. The sliding ways, with the cradles dogged to them, were in turn held in place on the groundways by large dogs with wedges fitted behind them. At launching time these dogs were driven out by the wedges. The forward end of the sliding ways was secured in some way, often by lashing to a stout post set in the ground at the head of the slip. At launching, usually half an hour before high water, the dogs holding the sliding ways were driven out by the wedges under them, leaving the whole weight on the lashing under the ship's bow. This was cut with an adze, and the ship slid down the ways into the water. A stout hawser from the stem to a bollard or post on shore helped to recover her, as well as acting as a drag. As the weight came off the cradle so it came to pieces, all the parts having been roped together to make recovery simple. Drags of chain or rope were used when the ways were long or steep, sometimes with baulks of timber lashed into bales. Side launching used four or more launchways, with cradles designed to carry the ship at right-angles to the keel blocks.

Side launch of the sailing barge *Kimberley*, Harwich, 1900

There were variations of the technique of launching from yard to yard, and the one I have quoted is only one typical example. In some places a 'patent release gear', generally using some form of trigger release, was used instead of the rope lashing. This was sometimes known as the 'launching poppet'.

In most yards the staging used during construction was temporary, put up to suit each vessel. Many of the larger yards had sets of permanent upright posts set along each side of the slips to which staging was fastened as needed. Some of these posts were properly made wooden box girders, but more often they were simply trees of about fifteen inches diameter at the butt, cleaned of bark and with the lower parts coated with tar. Similarly the shores used to support the ship on the slip were round, straight branches cleaned of bark. Many of the nineteenth-century yards had quay walls built between the slips, and this gave a stone facing to the sides of at least part of the building slip. It was not unknown for small vessels to be built between these walls using no more than

47

breast shores between the wall and the hull. In covered building sheds staging was usually fitted to the upright roof supports.

Sawpits also had their various forms, some being dug into the ground and lined with bricks or planks, some being built against a bank with the ends open, and others again built above ground on a trestle or with two stone side walls. The last two types had the advantage of being easier to clear of sawdust than those sunk in the ground. But there was always the problem of handling timber up to the top. Perhaps the most commonly favoured were those built against a bank with the top cleared, but it was not always possible. While the old sawpits remained in use in many places well into the present century, a surprising number of small yards had adopted steam saws before the middle of the nineteenth century. Timber scraps, sawdust and tree bark fed the boilers, which were fitted with prominent spark guards on the smokestacks. Failure to fit these led to disaster by fire more than once. The first steam saws were used mainly for reducing the whole log to thick planks, and for this reason were known as logsaws. The blade was straight and parallel-sided, usually working horizontally with a reciprocating action. Some of the very earliest worked vertically, being essentially powered versions of the pitsaw. Indeed, this was a hangover from still earlier sawmills using horse or water power, which also worked vertically. Some were fitted as gang saws, with several blades set to a gauge to produce a series of planks of equal thickness from one cut. The log was drawn under the saw on a trolley. This might be hauled by a geared-down steam winch, but more often it ran down a slope under the weight of the log, the speed being controlled by counterweights. Some of these saws remained in use until fairly recently, being modified in some yards by the addition of electric motors and handling gear. Some yards continued to use the older methods of sawing until electric machinery and suitable power supplies were available. In the earlier years of the twentieth century a great many had DC motors to suit locally generated power; others with more substantial financial resources built their own powerhouses and went over to electric plant almost entirely within the first two decades of the present century.

Buildings were often of a very rudimentary nature. When two-storeyed buildings were erected it was common practice to have workshops and stores on the ground floor, with possibly a 'dry' store and what passed for the 'office' above. Part or all of the top floor might be used as a mould loft or sail loft. Sometimes the loft was formed by flooring over the roof space below a highly pitched roof, and adding a few roof lights.

48

Figure 10 (a)   A small Westcountry shipyard, *circa* 1870

Figure 10 (b)   Shipbuilding on the beach in the Westcountry, *circa* 1780

Buildings were adapted as often as not, rather than purpose built. Figure 10(a) shows a former small West Country riverside yard built on a disused quay. In earlier days the quay with its small complex of cottages and warehouses handled farm produce and sand brought downriver for the nearby town of Dartmouth, and it was also used for landing sand and gravel dredged from the river for building purposes. By the mid-nineteenth century the quay and warehousing were disused, and soon converted to suit the needs of the shipyard. In one place the quay wall was broken roughly away to provide a building slip, and another was laid down on the beach beside it. A steam saw was installed in the small building on the extreme right. This particular yard was that of John Houston, at Higher Sandquay, Dartmouth, Devon, on the site of which now stands the dockyard belonging to the Britannia Royal Naval College. Part of the extreme left end of the block of cottages still stands, but this is all. Rail communication to Totnes, higher up the River Dart, brought an end to the practice of sending produce to Dartmouth for shipping coastwise, and the quay was available for Houston to build his yard in the 1860s.

Figure 10(b) is of an even smaller yard, again in the West Country, but almost a century earlier, in 1780. This time the site is on an open beach with little protection from the sea. The vessel on the stocks has a very simple staging around it, and the timber stocks are on the open beach—one hopes above high water. Presumably one of the cottages belonged to the shipwright, and the sawpit was probably in his yard. There is no sign of any other shipyard structures, sheds or workshops of any kind. This must have been typical of many small yards throughout Britain at that time. The whole place has greatly changed since either Stephen Richardson or his father, who are believed to have been the shipwrights there, built on this open beach. For this was the tiny hamlet of Torre Quay, and the view shows the site of what is now the Strand and Harbour, Torquay, Devon. In those days it was a very small place compared with the neighbouring shipping centres of Brixham and Dartmouth.

The term 'loft' occurs in a number of the maritime trades. There is the mould loft, the sail loft and the rigging loft. This seems to have arisen because a roof space provided the largest clear run of covered floor space in dry condition that could be found. I have already mentioned the use of a loft with workshops below. These structures were strongly built, but damp-proof courses were unknown and the ground floor was usually floored with beaten earth. This made it quite unsuited for either sail-making or moulding. 'Moulding' or 'lofting' entailed drawing out the lines of the vessel full size, then making light wooden templates from which the ship's timbers were cut. Some yards used a scrieve board built at the head of the building slip, on which the lines of a half-breadth of the ship were cut. When the ship was finished and a new one started the board, of smooth planking, was planed off and the new lines cut in for the next vessel. Smaller portable scrieve boards were also used, and still are. Although the scrieve board is still used in some parts of the world, it is not entirely satisfactory. The British climate, among other things, not always being conducive to outdoor work on the board, a more suitable answer was found in the use of a large wooden floor laid down in the loft over other premises. Here it was possible to work every-thing out in chalk, even the form of the bow and stern, under cover. Not only was this more convenient in allowing larger sections to be worked out, but it protected the floor from workmen's boots and the builder's secrets were protected from prying eyes. Thus arose the mould loft, with its wooden floor, as smooth as any dance floor, to take chalk lines and nails to guide the battens used for drawing curves. Many loftsmen wore canvas shoes to protect their floors, others worked bare-foot.

The sailmaker, too, needed a large dry area in which to work. Untreated sailcloth stored in the damp quickly becomes mildewed and rotten, and treatments to prevent this were almost unknown at the beginning of the last century. Sails in the completed form were treated in oak bark and ochre, when for fishing vessels, but rolls of unworked sailcloth were not treated. Rope and canvas made from hemp ran the risk of spontaneous combustion; damp fishing nets of hemp have caused many a fire at sea. So the sailmaker also adopted the loft, giving him a large, dry area clear of pillars and obstructions. The rigger, whose work in many ways was complementary to that of the sailmaker, needed a loft partly to keep his stocks of rope dry, and partly to provide the length he needed to work in. He was not so much concerned with the width, but the clean, dry length he needed was again best found up in the loft. Partly because their work was so closely associated, and partly because of their different needs of the loft, riggers and sailmakers often shared the same premises, the riggers working down one side while the sailmaker used the rest of the floor area.

So the loft became a universal and almost indispensable part of every

51

Figure 11 (a)   Wooden loft built on converted stone-built cottage base

Figure 11 (b)   Covered building slips with cill covered by the tide at
high water

shipbuilding establishment, for moulding or 'lofting', for sailmaking and for rigging. Even after the development of more modern styles of building, these rather specialised workshops were, and still are, known as lofts, though the building may be of only one storey or on the ground floor. Figure 11(a) shows a typical small shipyard adaptation, with a wooden loft built on top of a cottage base. This may have been a single-storeyed cottage, or the top floor may have been derelict when the yard was established.

It is extremely difficult to follow up the history of the small ship and boat yards. In almost every case there are long breaks in the use of a site, no records of any nature in writing, drastic alterations have been made or the site has returned to nature. Little seems to be known except what can be drawn from living memories, and even when first-hand these can prove unreliable. A few isolated pointers suggest that a high proportion of sites have been in use for many generations, and by many different families of shipwrights. The site might pass through several generations from father to son, then suddenly fall into disuse, perhaps through death, bankruptcy or the ending of a lease. Some yards remained closed and disused for many years, only to be reopened by some enterprising young shipwright with aspirations to become a master. There are old sayings in various parts of the country which imply that the industry had its fair share of slump years. Each seems to recognise a seven-year cycle. In the nineteenth century the main shipyards of Dartmouth, Devon, were in a part of the town known as Sandquay, and a local newspaper of 1862, when the yards were virtually empty, quoted a local verse:

> Each seven years, come what may,
> The grass will grow on Sandquay Quay.

From elsewhere similar rhymes are recorded, all implying the same fate:

> Seven years living lavish,
> Seven years on the parish.

or this rather doubtful one which I came across in some old notes from the East Coast which does not really sound quite genuine:

53

First year fighting all the way,
Second year spent in making hay,
Third and fourth and fifth he waxes,
Sixth year paying heavy taxes,
Seventh year come and he do fall,
No more boats to build at all.

This was scribbled on the back of an unreceipted bill for nails, and I get the impression that it was the product of an idle mind rather than the genuine article.

Some larger yards included as part of their establishment a range of workshops including all sail and rigging lofts, smithies, block and spar shops, etc, and employed their own craftsmen in all trades. Others had the premises but rented them out to various master craftsmen who worked mainly on the vessels built in the yard. These were virtually communal shipyards, the available work all going to the tenants of the premises. Some built their vessels in small dry docks, after the fashion once used widely by the Admiralty; others relied upon the cheaper and simpler slipways which did not call for massive excavation. As the nineteenth century progressed the tendency was for smaller craft to be built under cover in sheds. This had been pioneered by the Admiralty with some enormous wooden sheds in the naval dockyards. Shipbuilders tendering for naval small craft contracts found themselves obliged to build under cover, and covered slips such as that in Figure 11(b) sprang up in many places. These were invariably cheaply built of wood, with heavy tarpaulin curtains at the lower end. The roof usually followed the line of the slipway. The cill was covered at high water, and the launchways were laid out over the edge of the cill. Smaller craft were seldom accorded the traditional launching ceremony, but simply winched down the slipway. Modern equivalents of the building sheds are steel framed, clad in corrugated steel sheets or corrugated asbestos. The older wooden sheds usually had vertical planking sides rather than shiplap or weatherboarding. This was partly to facilitate replacement, though this was seldom carried out, and at the same time to present an end grain to the ground. The theory was that this would help to drain the wood after immersion at high tide, since the lower parts of most of the sheds were under water then. Glazing in the earlier sheds right up to the turn of the twentieth century consisted of small panes of glass fitted between vertical glazing bars. The pieces overlapped all the way

54

Part of Richard Dunston's yard, Thorne, Yorks

down, rather like slates on a roof. The pieces were seldom more than twelve inches wide, more often of the order of six inches. The only horizontal members of the window frame were the top and bottom bars.

The small yards with only one slip were often found in groups, and amalgamation made it possible to extend the yard considerably. Duplication of sheds was not necessary, and space now became available for sawmills and timber stacks. This in turn opened up wider scope for the men employed. Speculative building work, when orders were slack, now became a possibility. In places where land was available the yards were not so limited as those built on rocky shores or steep banks. When one suitable site became overcrowded, or a new craftsman wanted to become a master and could not find a site in the traditional place, he might well search for a completely new site and set up at some small distance from the home port. Here, if he did well, he might be able to take in more and more land, build more slips and quays, and over the course of twenty years or so acquire quite an extensive shipyard. Amalgamation had the disadvantage of killing competition within the port, and the independent craftsmen were at the mercy of one master. This included not only the men directly employed in the shipyards, but especially the many independent sailmakers, riggers, smiths and others who depended upon the yards for their work.

Many of the smaller ports were minor industrial complexes in their own right. The major trade in these settlements was obviously that of shipwright, especially when a man became a master craftsman. He might buy, inherit or perhaps marry into a yard of his own, or he might lease one. His customers would be drawn from the fishermen and merchant ship owners of the town or village and its vicinity. If he built up a reputation for good workmanship, quality, reliability or some exceptional feature of design he might well start to take orders from further afield. Successful tendering for Admiralty contracts would entitle him to put 'Contractor to the Admiralty' on his letterhead, if he used one, or advertise the fact on his nameboard over the gate. And so it could build up. He would probably be a working shipwright in his own yard for the greater part of his time, with a handful of men, shipwrights, sawyers, apprentices and a few labourers working for and with him. For the other essential components of his finished product he would depend upon outside men. His ironwork would be fashioned by a blacksmith who specialised in the various ship fittings, and was sometimes known as a shipsmith or trawlersmith, depending upon his particular field. Sails would be made by a local sailmaker working in his own loft, and rigging similarly would be contracted out. The shipwright might make his own spars, buying the blocks and deadeyes out, or he might call on the block and spar maker. Certainly this craftsman would be called upon to make the ship's pumps. Lamps and other items, made of sheet metal, tinplate or copper, might be made by a local tinsmith or coppersmith, and in fitting out a whole host of local traders would be called upon. The rigger might have his ropes from a local ropewalk, if there was one, and such things as hampers, maunds, fish baskets and a host of other items would come from the basketmaker. All the contractors would in turn call upon others to supply their requirements, and perhaps we should remember the ship's chandler, whose symbol of a woman holding a purse, often carved like a ship's figurehead, was found in many of the small ports of Britain.

All these people were dependent to a considerable extent upon the goodwill of the master shipwright, and slackness in the building yards meant that a great part of the community suffered. At times there was

56

discord between the trades, and many a good craftsman was forced out of business through some petty upset with a shipbuilder, when personal pride was too hard to swallow. But the communities were also endowed with a strength of their own which enabled them to survive in some places into the twentieth century.

· Ships built for people within the community were commonly financed by mortgage within the community. The man would be well known to all his neighbours—a feature of small communities the world over— and his character and abilities would be common knowledge. His new ship and several of his initial voyages would be financed and victualled on a credit basis. A proportion of the profits of each voyage were then set aside until the whole debt was cleared. This frequently happened within two or three years of the vessel being built. The same group of men would also contribute to speculative building, when work was slack, simply to hold the workforce and the community together until better times. It was not unknown for one of the more prosperous of the local craftsmen to be approached at such a time with the suggestion that he have a ship built for him. If he declined he might be told quite bluntly that there would be no more work for him in the port. This may smack of blackmail, and is certainly a dubious business practice, but it helped to keep the community going. In fact the vessel was almost always sold to another buyer before being launched. The working communities were housed in a motley collection of buildings, sometimes piled up together, sometimes spread throughout the town. Certain trades seem to have huddled together in some places for their mutual convenience, forming a group within which customers could be passed from one to the other with the minimum of delay. Some craftsmen set up their workshops on land adjoining their homes, or moved into cottages with suitable workshops attached. Sail lofts and smithies were often found in close proximity, though obviously the fumes and dust precluded the loft being actually over the forge. Nevertheless, a wall adjoining a smithy seems to have been considered an asset which may have contributed to the dryness of the loft.

Ropewalks were rather specialised buildings not found in every small port. Some of the larger places had five or six, producing rope and cordage for quite a large area. The walks varied in type and length, some being only a hundred yards or so long, others up to half a mile. The geography of the coastline had a lot to do with the length of the walk and its siting. On the fairly level land on the east coast of England long walks quite close to the sea could be expected. But in hilly country such as parts of the Scottish coast, and in Devon and Cornwall, where the coast is riven by steep valleys or coombs, level ground of any great extent is usually man-made. As such it was, and is, valuable for other aspects of maritime activity, and ropewalks were rarely able to find a footing there. The only other level sites might be found on the tops of adjacent hills, and a number of West Country ropewalks were so sited. On a map dated 1779 showing the town of Great Yarmouth, Norfolk, several ropewalks are shown built just outside the town walls near what was then known as Ropemaker's Gate. On the Ordnance Survey map of 1885 the ropewalks are still there, but almost lost sight of among newer buildings and dwellings. Some of the walks were transferred further out from the town centre at a later date, and the ropemakers received compensation for the move from the Corporation of Great Yarmouth.

At Brixham, in South Devon, the little harbour was served by two ropewalks during the opening years of the nineteenth century. One of these, only about 200 feet long, was right down by the sea. The other, roughly 700 feet long, was on the top of one of the two hills which overlook the harbour. In the 1840s it was realised that these two walks were quite inadequate to meet the needs of the extensive fishing fleet and a large fleet of local merchant schooners, and at the same time to provide part of the needs of the nearby town of Dartmouth, which had only one small walk. Consequently two new walks were built, each between 900 and 1,000 feet long, one on each of the two hilltops. The smallest walk was abandoned, and by 1855 the site had been built over. The old 700 feet walk continued rather longer, but by 1870 it, too, had fallen into disuse and was pulled down. The other two walks continued to operate into the twentieth century, the last of them closing just before the outbreak of World War I.

The structure of ropewalks varied as much as any other type of building. In some cases the buildings really were the barest minimum. The simplest ropewalk made use of a village sidestreet or lane, as shown in Figure 12. The drawing is a reconstruction based on information passed on to me many years ago by an old seaman in Looe, Cornwall. I made a rough sketch at the time, and the drawing is a cleaned-up version of that sketch. The original was approved by my informant, whose name I never found out. He was a Cornishman who had worked under sail all round the British coasts and into the Mediterranean,

Figure 12 Ropewalk in a village 'back lane', with a paved walk, wheel-house, tar-pot shed with its chimney and stakes in the side wall. The right side is flanked by occupied cottages

though not a native of Looe. He gave no definite information as to the location of the original of my sketch as far as I can recall, other than to say that this type of walk existed in many of the smaller seaport villages. One side of the lane was lined with cottages, the other bounded by a stone wall. Into the wall were driven the stakes upon which the strands were supported as they were spun up. At the far end are the gear sheds, one containing the winding gear, the other the sledge and other gear. Behind the sheds can be seen the chimney of the tar copper. These very simple ropewalks were probably only used intermittently, as cordage was required, hence the unsophisticated layout. This type of walk was probably the property of a local roper who supplemented his income by renting his cottages.

Larger walks sometimes had little more than a shed to house the tar pots and winding gear, and the walk itself was completely open with stakes driven into the ground or a convenient wall along the whole length of it. In some places the walk itself ran along a beach, if it were a suitable wide flat one. The better walks had roofing over the entire length, but were usually open down one side with pillars to support the roof. This was a matter of building economy, saving on a wall and roof-lights. At each end would be a short area completely walled, one of which would house the winding gear. The tar pots or coppers were usually separately housed, with a stout capstan supported partly by the roof timbers for hauling heavy cables through the hot tar. The copper was supported on a stone fireplace with a stone chimney. There might be two such pots, one equipped for heavy cables, the other for light cables and yarns. The smaller one would be fitted up with a windlass for hauling the cordage through. Cast iron pots were used during the nineteenth century, though they might well have been of copper at one time. Very few of the ropewalks were completely closed in, owing to the danger of spontaneous combustion of the hemp. With open sides it was simple to drag the offending coils or stacks out to reduce the danger to the rest of the stock.

The standard length of a coil of rope is 120 fathoms, or 720 feet, which calls for the twisting of strands of a very much greater length. Some of the large inland walks were up to half a mile long. A combination of the British climate and an open walk of that length suggests that ropewalking was not all that pleasant in winter.

The block maker's premises were not particularly large or spectacular, unless he happened to have a stockyard or log pond. Generally he fashioned the spars in the yard where the vessel was being built, working as near to the ship as possible to save unnecessary handling. The largest job likely to be carried out in the blockshop itself might be the boring of pump barrels, and even this was often done on site. The block maker frequently made pumps. These were for the bilge pumps, and consisted of a wooden barrel some twelve to fourteen feet long, fitted with a plunger containing a one-way flap valve. The water passed through the valve on the downstroke of the plunger, and was lifted on the upstroke. When sufficient water had accumulated on top it poured out of a lip on the top of the pump barrel and over the ship's deck. The pumps were usually fitted in pairs worked by a rocker arm over the top. After about 1820 spars and pumps made up the bulk of the block maker's work. As already pointed out, this was due to the mass production of the majority of normal sizes of blocks. The block maker also made wooden waterpipes, boring them from the trunks of elm trees, but this was another dying trade as metal pipes came more widely into use. The space required for boring a pump barrel need only be about twice that of the length of the barrel, but few of the blockshops had this available. It could be carried out on site or in a street or passageway.

Although coppersmiths and tinsmiths were not particularly maritime tradesmen, those that lived and worked in the ports of Britain naturally tended to specialise in the requirements of the maritime industries, just as the blacksmith did. Many of their products were used in fitting out, such as lamps, flare cans, kettles, cooking pots, frying pans, tin boxes, sea chests, oil cans and so on. They would be called on to make stove pipes and metal ventilator tops, and to supply metal coamings to fit round through-deck fittings. One regular job for the coppersmith was the windvane for the masthead, popularly known as a 'wift'.

Again the shops were generally small, allowing for little more than a store and a small working area. The larger tools might include a forge, a bench, shears and perhaps small rolls, typical of the sheet metal worker's trade. Often one whole wall of the workshop consisted of a pair of large doors. The main purpose of these was not the manhandling of large items in and out, but the provision of ventilation. The fumes in a low-roofed coppershop are thick and most unpleasant. A wicket door in one of the large doors provided for normal access.

The basketmaker was found in every maritime community, not only serving the village and district with the normal demands of basketry, but producing a range of goods for seafarers. Fishing communities

BARREL MAKERS. GREAT HERRING INDUSTRY AT LOWESTOFT.   215

Coopers at Lowestoft, about 1900

perhaps had more call on the basketmaker's talents than the merchant centres but even there he was in demand, particularly because his products had a relatively short life. He usually worked in a small workshop attached to his home, and was often to be seen working sitting on his front doorstep. Among his products were several sizes of maund, used for handling bulk goods on and off ship, various sizes and types of fishbasket (crans, half-crans, kits, pads, half-pads, etc), lunch baskets, hampers, some types of cargo containers, strainers for the bottom intakes of bilge pumps, and in some fishing communities he also made crab and lobster pots and store pots, though in many places the fishermen made these themselves. The basketmaker's contribution to the life of a maritime community was quite important, and he deserves to be included among the maritime trades.

Another tradesman found in practically every maritime centre was the cooper. His products included barrels and casks of every kind, also mooring buoys, bailers and tubs. During the height of the great West Country pilchard trade, between 1500 and 1700, the demand for hogsheads was so great that ready-formed barrel staves were imported from Brittany by the thousand to be made up on the coasts of Devon and Cornwall.

These small maritime complexes are none too easy to trace today.

62

Larger ports have changed so much with the extension of port facilities, building of warehousing, amalgamation of shipyards, improved repair facilities for modern shipping, closures and infilling, that there are few of the really old workshops and yards left. Places such as London, Liverpool, Bristol and Southampton grew from such small beginnings, but their expansion started too early, and the alterations have been so drastic in the last century or so that there is little left today. It is in the smaller ports, many of which were of far greater importance in the maritime world than their appearance today would suggest, that traces can still sometimes be found. This is especially true of the West Country, where even some of the old wood shipbuilding skills still survive among the older men. It is still possible to find tiny boatsheds in various places on the Cornish coast, and on the Welsh and Scottish coasts, with a handful of men working in the old way. The conditions appear, to modern eyes, most primitive, and the craft are generally quite small, but they are built in the old way, with the assistance of electric lighting and perhaps a handful of electric drills. Many of the old skills still survive in such places, and some are being passed on to apprentices, but much of the knowledge accumulated over the centuries is and has been lost, through those skills no longer being needed. It is doubtful if they would be able to completely build a vessel in the traditional manner today.

If methods of working are at least in part being passed on, the tools are changing fast. No longer is the local blacksmith called on to make tools to measure, and the big toolmakers' catalogues no longer show the great range of shipbuilding tools made in the last century. Today it is a matter of ordering from a local tool stockist and hoping the tool you want is still in production. With the passing of the tools, as the traditional building methods give way to what are almost factory methods, so the skills themselves will eventually pass away completely. Fortunately we have been afforded a brief respite, for the construction of replica ships of earlier times in Devon of recent years has brought back, to some extent, some of those old skills, giving younger men a chance to learn something of them.

I would like to show an example of one of these small maritime communities, and I have chosen to use Brixham, in Devon, about the years 1840–50. Quite apart from the fact that I know the place very well, there are logical reasons for selecting it. During the period chosen Brixham was one of the most prosperous maritime centres on the south coast of England. There was a fleet of some 120 sailing trawlers of 20

The trawler-type yacht *Cachalot* about to be launched, Brixham, 1903

to 40 tons each, about 100 smaller fishing vessels fishing in almost every known way, and a fleet of about 140 merchant schooners working along the coast or to the Mediterranean, the Azores, Newfoundland, the West Indies, South America and elsewhere, of between 80 and 200 tons. The population at the time was under 6,000, yet in addition to the seagoing element there was a full supporting industrial centre in the old port. The schooners gradually died out from about 1870 on, but the sailing trawler fleet, for which Brixham became famous, waxed stronger still, declining just after World War I. There were still 16 of these vessels on register just prior to World War II. With the trawler fleet staying under sail so long, the shore-based supporting trades remained perhaps longer than in most places, and their concentration had for long been higher than in other places of equivalent size. Consequently until about 15 years ago it was still possible to find many of the workshops and premises of the swarm of small craftsmen who once worked there, and it was not difficult to find men who had worked in these trades. Today most of the old shops have been swept away in the interests of the tourist trade, making way for car parks and holiday flatlets and the like. I really could not think of any place in Britain which could illustrate the maritime community better. As a fishing port of historical and national importance, Brixham also had a number of features peculiar to trawling ports, such as barking yards, curing houses and beam yards.

The map in Figure 13 gives some idea of the density of the workshops, particularly in the level area in the valley to the south-west of the harbour. As late as 1781 this area was almost all used by the local basketmakers for growing withies, but from 1790 onwards was gradually reclaimed for building purposes. Earlier still it was a tidal mill dam used as an upper harbour. The whole area grew up as a maze of narrow alleys, few more than eight feet wide, rejoicing in names like Paradise Place and Furze's Alley. Most of them have vanished under modern clearance and development quite recently. Six or seven basketmakers were scattered among the community shown, but these have proved difficult to locate.

Figure 14 is a plan of Great Yarmouth, Norfolk, about 1619. Built on fairly flat land, it was a walled town, partially moated. One area of ropewalks is shown, just inside Ropemaker's Gate, others being built just outside it by 1779. Many other small workshops lay within the built-up area, and the boat yards were growing up on the north-east bank of the River Yare. There were also net chambers and herring curing houses—herring was the mainstay of the industry at the port. Brixham had the Devon equivalents of curing houses, pilchard cellars, from before 1500 onwards, but only one survived into the nineteenth century, and this ceased to operate about 1840. From 1958 to 1975 it housed Brixham Museum. The development of the trawl fishery at Brixham closed down old pilchard cellars such as this, but Yarmouth was dependent upon the herring well into the present century, though even here the tourist and holiday business has now taken over. Figure 15, dated at about 1870, shows the developments at Great Yarmouth which even then were evident. The old ropewalks inside the town walls were closed and new ones built further out. The net chambers, too, were moved well away to the south, but some shipsmiths and anchor-smiths remained among the buildings inside the line of the old town wall.

65

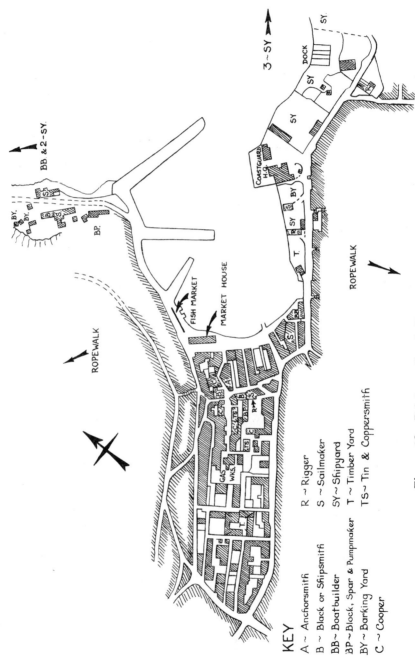

KEY

A ~ Anchorsmith
B ~ Black or Shipsmith
BB ~ Boatbuilder
BP ~ Block, Spar & Pumpmaker
BY ~ Barking Yard
C ~ Cooper

R ~ Rigger
S ~ Sailmaker
SY ~ Shipyard
T ~ Timber Yard
TS ~ Tin & Coppersmith

Figure 13 Brixham, South Devon, harbour area, 1840–50

The area to the north-east of the town had been laid out as streets, and the development of pleasure piers and gardens fronting the North Sea shows clearly that the holidaymaker was becoming important to the town. At the same time the shipyards had developed on both banks of the River Yare, and this area was destined to become the more industrialised part of the town, with the docks.

The trend today in almost all the coastal ports is to concentrate on catering for the holidaymaker. Dreams of quick fortunes in this field have brought to the coast new generations of hotel, holiday camp and guesthouse keepers, amusement caterers and café proprietors, mostly drawn from far inland. They have little knowledge of, or respect or appreciation for, the traditional crafts or the communal spirit which was such a feature of life in the old small ports. Except in the larger and more highly developed ports, craftsmen are being pushed further away from the coasts. The holiday industry campaigns against industries which could provide much-needed work for the local population, yet they are delighted if they can find an old building and convert it into, say, the

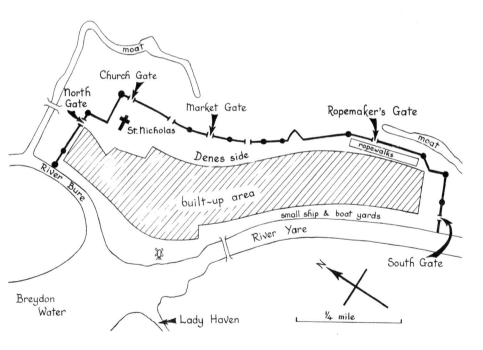

Figure 14   Great Yarmouth, circa 1619

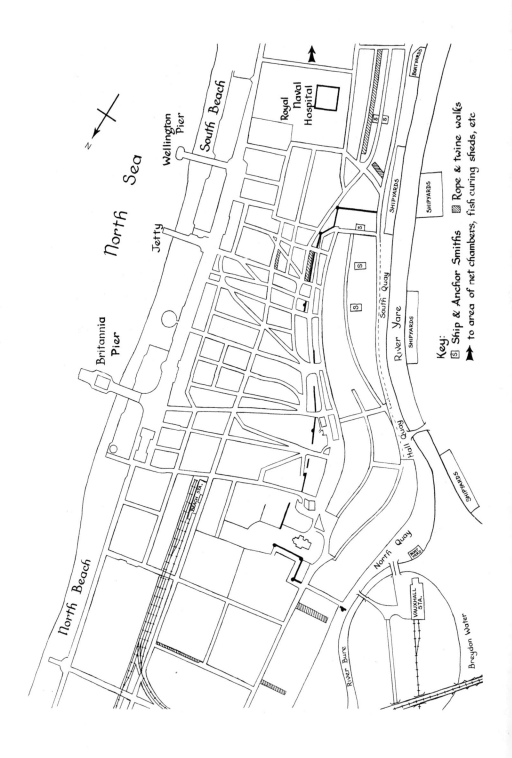

North Sea

North Beach

Britannia Pier

Jetty

Wellington Pier

South Beach

Royal Naval Hospital

BOATYARDS

SHIPYARDS

SHIPYARDS

South Quay

River Yare

SHIPYARDS

Hall Quay

SHIPYARDS

North Quay

BOAT YARD

River Bure

VAUXHALL STA.

Breydon Water

BEACH STA.

Key:
Ⓢ Ship & Anchor Smiths ▨ Rope & twine walks
➤ to area of net chambers, fish curing sheds, etc

'Sail Loft Café', and cash in on the trades they have to a great extent displaced.

The more sinister side to the change, however, is that young people looking for trades and professions with a future are driven to search far inland from the moment they leave school. Districts which once cried out for apprentices, and whose craftsmen were widely renowned for their skills, are now industrially and to a large extent socially derelict or unbalanced.

A few shipyards incorporating the ancilliary trades still survive, though they are growing fewer. The change-over by some yards to steel construction in the 1880s stood many in good stead until the mid-1950s, but many have since closed. World War II and the following period of full order books lulled several into a false sense of security. With Japanese and Continental competition, and the financial crises at home, the small British yards were in no position to meet the challenge. Old and worn-out machinery which had paid for itself many times over had, by the 1950s, become very expensive to replace, and its maintenance was just as prohibitive. Few could face the cost of retooling to meet foreign competition, and between 1955 and 1968 many yards either closed for good, after well over a century of practically continuous work, or turned to other work, to which, in most cases, they were quite unsuited.

(*opposite*) Figure 15   Great Yarmouth, *circa* 1870

3

TIMBER AND SAWING

Timber was formerly the basic raw material of shipbuilding. It is well-known that the voracious appetite of the navy in Britain devoured thousands of acres of prime timber, and it would appear that the small shipbuilders were left to make use of timber from the smaller estates and odd trees in copses and small woods. Secondhand timber bought from broken-up vessels was also available to them, and often enough perfectly sound timbers could be cut from the centres of heavy scantlings from old naval craft, large enough to use on smaller vessels. The naval construction programme, with its heavy demands for oak, looked for reasonably large estates with extensive stands of timber. The trouble involved in extracting timber in small quantities from a variety of places was beneath the consideration of the naval authorities, but the smaller shipbuilding concerns were not looking for timber in such vast quantities. It often happened that one small wood might yield enough mature oak and elm to meet the immediate demands of a yard at no great distance. By the nineteenth century a great deal of timber had grown up since the times of the great naval denudations, and rather more was available than in earlier centuries, thanks to judicious planting by far-sighted landowners. Also considerable quantities were being imported.

The mysteries of measuring standing timber are by no means as involved as might be thought. The old shipwrights and foresters used a simple but reasonably accurate method, provided the art of estimating both the height of the usable part of the tree, and the circumference at that height, had been mastered. Both these measurements having been estimated, the circumference at the base was measured. The mean of the two circumferences was taken, and one quarter of this mean, known as the 'quarter girt', was then multiplied by itself and the height to give a fair approximation of the cubic content of the tree. This was the old log measure, and logs after cutting were said to be 'bark on' or 'under

The boat shed at Richard Dunston's yard, Thorne

bark' depending upon their condition at the time of measuring. Trees
and logs are still measured by quarter girth and height or length. Oak
logs might well have been without bark, since this was in demand for
both the tanneries and for 'barking' the sails of fishing craft—the origin
of the tanned colour so commonly seen at one time. Felled timber was
simply measured for length and quarter girth at half the length, unless
the taper was excessively variable.

Timber was often ordered and referred to by the load, a unit that
was nominally fifty cubic feet. One tree could very well exceed this.

Owing to the shortage of home-grown timber, which made itself felt
as early as Tudor times, much timber used in merchant ships was
imported, and it was not unknown for several species of foreign hardwoods to be incorporated in one ship's structure. Softwoods were imported
from the Baltic and other places, and at one time these were purchased
from stacks on the docksides of the foreign ports. Timber was also bought
by the 'standard', which varied slightly in quantity from place to place.
The Petrograd standard, containing 165 cubic feet, became the norm
and is still used today. This curious measurement has caused many a
headache to timber buyers and their clerks.

71

In the shipyards the timber was also known under different names according to its size and purpose. 'Thick stuff' was plank of over 4in thick and up to 12in or more wide. Today its larger sizes might be termed baulk timber. 'Plank' was timber planking 1½–4in thick, and 'boards' were planks under 1½in thick. 'Compass' timbers were curved, suited to frames, and were also known as crooks or bends. Curved timbers could be either naturally grown shapes or they might have been from branches deliberately bent during growth to provide the curves the shipbuilders wanted. Smaller crooks were sharper and more angular, ideal for making heavy knees rather than frames.

It was common for the master shipwright or his foreman (who was often the power behind the design of a vessel) to go to the woods to select the trees. A contract would be drawn up with the owner, and arrangements made for felling, lopping and carting. If the woodland was fairly close to the yard the shipwrights might fell and lop the timber themselves, and arrange for a local carter to haul it to the yard. The Smith family, shipbuilders at Rye, Sussex, went to the Sussex Weald for their timber, cutting it with their own men and contracting out the haulage. To the west, in Devon, William Gibbs, who built at Galmpton Creek on the bank of the River Dart, had an even cheaper method. He bought standing timber from the stands of oak on the steep river bank around Sharpham, a few miles up-river. He was rowed up-river by a few of his shipwrights, selected his trees, felled and lopped them on the spot, then towed them back down-river to his yard. Gibbs was one of those men who built his own yard up from scratch in the fourth decade of the nineteenth century on a new site with room to expand, which he could not find in his native town of Brixham.

Whenever possible shipyards liked to have a log pond. For preference a log pond should have running water through it, though tidal conditions were suitable, provided that the timber did not dry out at low water. The ponds were usually formed of booms of logs chained or dogged together to prevent the loose logs inside from straying. Larger yards and the Royal Dockyards had specially constructed ponds with lock gates so that they were always full of water. The main purpose was to wash the sap out of the wood to facilitate seasoning. At the same time the wood was less likely to split than when it was dried out on land. After a suitable spell in the pond the logs were removed, dried out and sawn. The period varied according to the flow of water through the pond, the type of timber, and so on.

The whole question of seasoning timber for ship work is a rather difficult one. No two men seem to have had the same ideas. On land, some of the better timber stockyards would not intentionally sell timber they had not seasoned for several years, others considered a year sufficient. The demand for timber was such, however, that it was seldom allowed to lie in the stockyards for very long. Some buyers, particularly furniture makers, seasoned their own timber after purchase, and would then prefer it as green as possible. But in shipbuilding it was quite an accepted practice to frame up in green oak, and leave the ship, in frame only, to season on the stocks. To save on transport many heavier frames and other sections were roughed to shape in the woods before haulage to the yards. This was especially the case with large naval work. The waste was sold to local woodsmen for firewood or small constructional purposes to help defray the costs as much as possible.

The types of native timber mostly used in ship construction were oak, elm, larch (when of sufficient size and quality) and a certain amount of softwood such as Scots pine, usually referred to as fir. Beech, although prolific, was quite useless since it rots rapidly in water, though it is ideal for furniture making. Elm is the opposite, and thrives on submersion. Oak was the most widely used, and to augment supplies much was imported. Of the imported oaks, that from the Adriatic, probably the ilex or evergreen oak, was considered the best and was in great demand. It has good curving branches; some was grown in Britain expressly for shipbuilding. Oak also started to come in from Canada, in 1763, but it was found to be inferior, and subject to early decay, as was much of the oak from the Baltic. Danzig oak was sometimes used, but not for load-bearing structures. Larch, pitchpine, African oak and fir were all imported in considerable quantities, and about the middle of the nineteenth century teak from Burma started to reach Britain. It had already been used for shipbuilding in India for a very long time. American elm and the slightly harder and tougher Canadian rock elm were also used, and in fact elm from a variety of sources found its way into British shipyards in the early years of the nineteenth century. Another import of the mid-nineteenth century was mahogany, of the variety known as Honduras or Spanish, with a deep red colour.

During and after World War II the demand for timber was at a high level, and little homegrown timber was of a size suitable for Britain's shipyards. Many different types were imported from Africa, some being very useful, others of doubtful usefulness. Several mahogany types, especially gaboon, were used, and two or three substitutes for teak, such as iroko and afrormosia. Iroko is probably the better of these two for ship work, since afrormosia, though very handsome to start with, bleaches rather quickly and has a tendency to iron staining. Since it was intended to replace teak on yacht decks, this is an undesired trait. Teak itself is preferred, but its price reached such astronomical heights after World War II that many yards will not now consider it unless particularly specified.

The problems of decay in timber have always been a cause of concern among shipwrights. One way of delaying it which was tried was by charring. One side of the timber was kept against a fire while the other side was kept wet. There is some doubt as to whether this was actually to prevent decay or to aid bending or retaining curves in timber which was unseasoned. In Phineas Pett's journal for 1677 there is a note on a visit paid by Pett and Sir Anthony Deane to a woodland at Otley, where new timber was being cut for a new naval vessel. At Otley they found '. . . the Carters carrying away a stern post for the new ship at Harwich, and the rest converting on the ground, as fast as could be.' The actual shaping of the timber was being done in the woodland with the timber as green as it could be. If such timber was charred it might well stand up better than if left entirely green, and warping would take place at the fire rather than later.

Certainly for bending planks the method of charring seems to have been fairly universal until the early years of the eighteenth century, when an improved plan known as 'stoving' replaced it. This involved heating the planks in wet sand until they were sufficiently pliable to work into the ship. About the middle of the same century this was in turn superseded by the steam chest or kiln. This was a long box supplied with steam in which the planks were placed until pliable. The method is still in use, with metal chests being used.

Extracting the timber and carting it to the yards presented its own particular problems, and special vehicles were used. A certain amount of timber which could not be made use of was either left or sold to woodsmen, who would produce logs for firewood or billets for other rural craftsmen to use. Small branches were collected up for various purposes, often being bound up into faggots for firing. Bakers used large quantities of faggots for heating their ovens.

In Britain sawing was normally done on a sawpit, but this seems to have been peculiar to Britain and those countries upon which she had influence. The more usual method in Europe was to set up one trestle, or perhaps two of unequal height, and saw the timber at an angle to the ground. How Britain came to work differently is lost in the past, and it has certainly been British practice since at least 1500. There are very few illustrations of English sawing, but all show the timber horizontal, either above a pit or on two level trestles. European sawing, on the other hand, is fairly well illustrated, and always shows either one or two trestles, never a pit, with the plank or baulk at an angle.

There were a number of itinerant sawyers working throughout the British countryside in pairs, usually working for the small rural workshops on what might be called their 'circuit'. If pushed, the smaller shipyard might well employ a pair of these men to do part of their sawing. The trickier work, such as frames, would more likely be done by the yard men. George Sturt, in *The Wheelwright's Shop*, beautifully describes the activities of a pair of itinerant sawyers his father hired annually to saw his trees on the pit ready for seasoning, quite apart from their sawing prowess when they finally got down to it. The top sawyer was the head man, and he started by sharpening the saw, leaving the pitman or bottom sawyer to his own devices—in this case searching out the local inn. By the time the saw was ready the pitman was too drunk to work. While he sobered up, the top sawyer sampled the local brew until he, too, was in no condition to work. This might very easily go on for two or three days.

Sawing by any kind of power has a long history, albeit rather an obscure one. Wind-powered sawmills were known on the Continent during the thirteenth century. In 1322 at least one mill in Germany was powered by a water wheel, and this seems to be the earliest record of water power harnessed to sawing. In 1634 a water-powered sawmill was set up in America, at the falls of the Piscataqua, near the border of Maine and New Hampshire, and no doubt others followed in the productive forests of that country. Efforts to set up powered sawmills in England were not so successful. Opposition from the hand sawyers caused the abandonment of a water sawmill in 1663, and no further attempts were made for over a century. Then, in 1768, a water sawmill was erected at Limehouse, which at the time was outside London. It either never worked or only operated for a short time. A mob supporting the interests of the hand sawyers destroyed it. Powered mills were certainly in use in Britain before the end of the eighteenth century, in spite of the opposition. Perhaps because of their lower capacity there does not seem to have been the same kind of opposition to sawmills operated by horse-gins, which were powered by anything from one to four horses.

Early sawmills went through a variety of stages. The Tudor hand mills were built in the form of a large shed, with a complete grillage of beams set across them at about six or seven feet from the floor. Many logs at a time could be sawn by pitsaw, each handled by the usual two men, all over this grill. The first powered mills used a gatesaw, which was no more than a frame saw running in guides, operated from below by an eccentric. This was simpler to arrange in a water mill than a windmill. The saw worked vertically just as the pitsaw did, and the lower operating wheel took its name from the man it replaced—the pitman. Another early saw was not strictly mechanical, and being a hybrid type of machine it became known as the muley saw. The muley saw consisted of a frame saw operated by one man. The frame worked in guides and was heavily counterweighted so that very little weight fell on the sawyer. His stroke was a downward pull, the saw being returned by the counterweight beams.

The gangsaw was a development of the gatesaw, and might well be considered a large version of the hand veneer-cutting saws used by furniture makers during the eighteenth century, with many equally-spaced blades. The gate was fitted with a series of blades, anything from one to twenty, and again worked vertically. The result was an early form of mass-produced planking, and it was probably more employed in the production of house-building timber, such as wainscoting, than for ships' timbers.

Patent machinery, which included saws, was installed in both the major blockmaking concerns in England by the 1770s. The establishment of Walter Taylor at Southampton, principal blockmaking contractors to the Admiralty from 1759 to 1805, used water power. That of Dunstanville at Plymouth, using rather similar machinery, was horse powered. The first circular saw is thought to have been invented by Walter Taylor for use in his block mills, possibly as early as 1770. For larger sawmills the circular saw remained really experimental until about 1855, though some of the smaller mills working on small sizes of timber seem to have adopted it fairly widely soon after 1800, and especially when steam power was utilised. Steam engines for sawing came into use between 1825 and 1830, though water power, and where water was scarce, the horse, remained the principle source of sawmill power until about 1835. Steam took over rapidly after that. By the 1850s even some of the small ship-yards had a steam saw. Most of the early steam saws still worked either vertically or, more frequently, horizontally. Nearly all were log saws using a parallel blade which was pulled through the wood on the cutting stroke. These old steam saws were really robustly built, and many of them did yeoman service for something like eighty years or more. It must be admitted, however, that most of them were rather like the proverbial old hammer, with a new head and a new handle, towards the end of their working days.

Bandsaws were a later development which could not come about until new metallurgical techniques produced a reliable steel suitable for the blades. At first produced for cutting profiles in wood, they soon improved into a range of large saws capable of sawing wood, plastics or metal. Today logsaws of the bandsaw type are in widespread use, and of very large size. The saw has returned to the vertical position, though no longer reciprocating, and a mechanically propelled carriage carries the logs past the saw blades. The blades are sharpened automatically on a sharpening and resetting machine on which the blade runs horizontally and an arm bearing a file takes one stroke at a time over each tooth at a precise angle. The setting is done by a pair of anvils working against each other as the saw moves on one tooth-space at a time. A far cry from the old ways, and strictly beyond the scope of our present study.

THE FIGURES

Figure 16   These two illustrations were made from aquatints dating from the first twenty years of the nineteenth century. The tools themselves are none too well delineated, but the purpose of the drawings was as a guide to artists, and not necessarily too accurate in detail.

Figure 16(a)   Logs being trimmed and split, and faggots being collected. Two axes, of a type that seems to be a cross between the Kent and American patterns, two beetles or 'bittles' (large wooden mallets) with the heads bound in iron, which were used to drive splitting wedges, and a simple 'horse' to support the logs are shown.

Figure 16(b)   A crosscut saw is here being used to cut up logs. The principal horse here is a pile of logs, rather too high and far from the saw to be of value; it looks as if the log will soon start to sag and the saw to bind.

77

(a)

trimming logs: note beetles for splitting and simple 'horse'

(b)

crosscutting: using a two-man crosscut saw and an improvised 'horse'

Figure 16   In the woodlands

(a)

5"
to
12"

splitting or cleaving
wedges

(b)

Kent axe head

(c)

'Northern' Kent axe
with capped poll

(d)

Kent pattern felling axe

(e)

American pattern felling axe

Figure 17   Timber cutting

Figure 17(a)   The usual forms of splitting or cleaving wedges used for cleaving wood with the grain. Cleft timber, because it follows the natural grain of the wood, is structurally stronger than sawn timber, and was generally preferred for many purposes. The wedges were either iron or steel, and did not always have a groove down them. Like many other tools, they were often made by the local blacksmith.

Figure 17(b) The standard 'Kent pattern' axehead. I have not been able to discover how this name came to be given to this axe, and can only suggest that it is a design from an iron works in the Weald of Kent which was later taken up by the bigger tool manufacturers. The head was made in several weights and with a number of haft sizes, but was generally used like a hatchet for general trimming and light woodcutting.

Figure 17(c) The 'Northern Kent' axe, with the usual form of haft. In this variety of the axe the poll was reinforced with hardened steel to take the shock and wear when the axe was used for cleaving.

Figure 17(d) The 'Kent pattern' felling axe, a well balanced tool with a rather straighter haft than is usual nowadays.

Figure 17(e) This type of felling axe is known in the toolmaking trade as 'American', though the origin of this is again not clear. It is thought to be an older style than the Kent axe, derived from an axe with a wider cutting edge but without the cheek usual in the Kent pattern. Formerly extensively used, its compact shape made it ideal for export owing to its convenience for packing. If large numbers were exported to America this may well have been the origin of the name. This and the Kent pattern were the two main types used in English woodlands for the greater part of the nineteenth century. Hafts of all the English axes were commonly made of ash, though towards the end of the nineteenth century, when there appears to have been a shortage of suitable home-grown ash, imported American hickory came to be used for the cheaper tools.

Figure 18(a) An early handsaw illustrated in the Bedford Book of Hours of 1423. This is a pull saw, in spite of its unlikely-looking handle. It is obviously related to the Viking 'bread-knife' saw in Figure 9(g), with the reversed teeth of the Bronze Age saw. It is, I suppose, possible that if saws of this form were used in Saxon times, then some of them could easily have been wrongly identified as domestic utensils.

Figure 18(b) A crosscut saw shown in a late fifteenth-century engraving by Botticelli of the prophet Isaiah. The method of fitting the handles is obviously an artistic interpretation, but the curving back and the straight or 'two-hand' set of the teeth look authentic. These tools have not really changed very much.

Figure 18(c) This curious saw is from an engraving by Sadelerus, after M. de Vos, of about 1580. The handle fitting may be authentic, though in rather a more slender form than the real thing, but the teeth are most

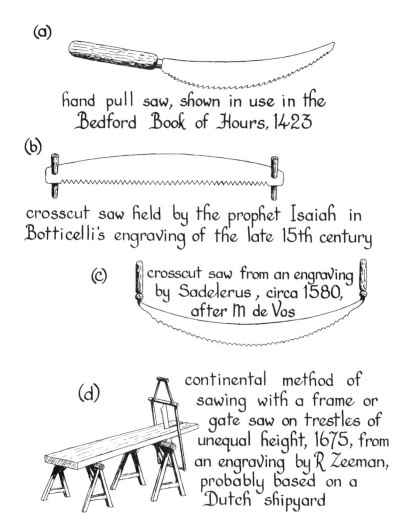

hand pull saw, shown in use in the
Bedford Book of Hours, 1423

(b)

crosscut saw held by the prophet Isaiah in
Botticelli's engraving of the late 15th century

(c)   crosscut saw from an engraving
       by Sadelerus, circa 1580,
            after M de Vos

(d)   continental method of
       sawing with a frame or
       gate saw on trestles of
       unequal height, 1675, from
       an engraving by R Zeeman,
       probably based on a
       Dutch shipyard

Figure 18   Some old saws

unusual, which again could be artistic licence. They are set from each end, so that there is a short area of two-hand in the centre, but as the saw sweeps out towards its ends the rake gradually turns in to the centre. If this was true, then it would imply that the saw only really cut for half of its stroke.

Figure 18(d)   Taken from a well-known engraving by R. Zeeman, dated 1675, this was found among the engravings—in fact it was their

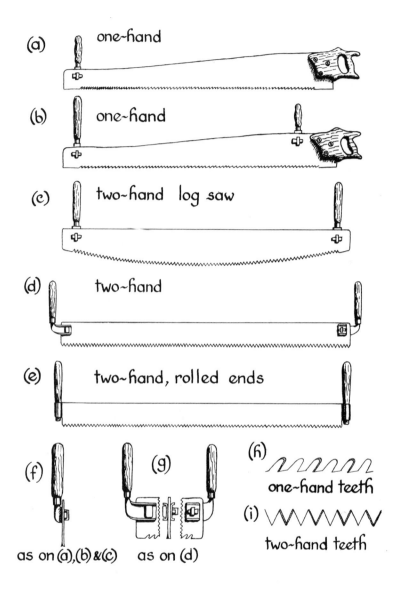

(a) one-hand

(b) one-hand

(c) two-hand log saw

(d) two-hand

(e) two-hand, rolled ends

(f)

(g)

(h) one-hand teeth

(i) two-hand teeth

as on (a),(b)&(c)   as on (d)

Figure 19   Crosscut saws

frontispiece—bound up with Sir Anthony Deane's manuscript in the Pepysian Library, Magdalene College, Cambridge. I have seen this sawing set-up used to illustrate British shipbuilding of the period, but this is in fact the European style, not the English. The engraving probably illustrates a Dutch shipyard, partly from the sawing method (with a frame saw on trestles of unequal height), partly from the view of a Dutch ship (probably a type known as a flute, peculiar to the Netherlands) in the background, and partly because of the engraver's name, which sounds very Dutch. The sketch shows clearly that the trestles were quite unequal, and the frame saw has a wide blade, not the narrow type used in English frame saws—which is why the frame was used.

Figures 19(a) and (b)   Two of the commonest forms of the one-hand crosscut saw. The terms 'one-hand' or 'two-hand' do not apply to the number of hands needed to hold the saw, nor to the number of men needed to use it, but to the set of the saw teeth. One-hand teeth would only cut one way, two-hand teeth were set without rake, so that the saw would cut on either stroke. Most one-handed crosscuts had a handle rather like that on the ordinary carpenter's hand saw, with a post handle at either one end or both, depending upon the size. Lengths of five or six feet were about normal for this saw.

Figures 19(c), (d) and (e)   Three forms of log saw, all of which cut two-handed. There was another form with the top edge curved and the teeth in a straight line. The last of these three is probably the oldest, with the ends simply rolled round to provide a socket for the post handles, which were jammed down as tightly as possible. The other two exhibit different versions of handle fitting.

Figures 19(f) and (g)   The two methods of fitting handles that were the most common in the nineteenth century. Both are very similar. The first makes use of a slotted lug on the side of the handle shaft which fitted through a slot in the saw. It was held in place by a tapered steel wedge through the slot and flat against the face of the saw. The second type is probably the later one, and utilised a plate handle with a slot and a small backing plate with a slot. A separate shaped pin went through both these slots and a slot in the saw. This pin was retained again by a tapered steel wedge.

Figures 19(h) and (i)   The two most usual forms of one-hand and two-hand teeth. There were several styles of tooth outline, but these were the most commonly used. Every saw maker had his own pet style, each

83

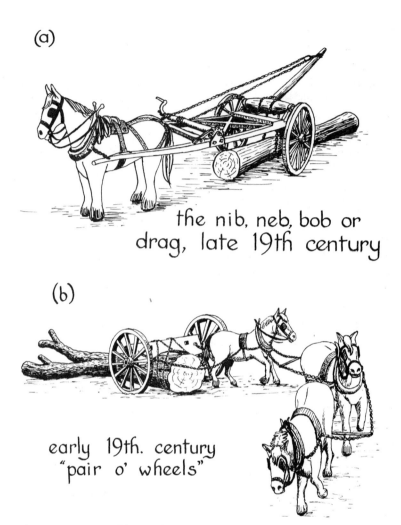

(a)

the nib, neb, bob or
drag, late 19th century

(b)

early 19th. century
"pair o' wheels"

Figure 20   Timber transport

claiming to be better than its rivals, but they really were quite alike. Those saws intended for really rough work had deeply gulleted teeth, perhaps set in pairs as in the 'great American tooth'. This was intended mainly for the fast cutting of softwood trees, but most of Britain's trees were hardwood, calling for finer teeth, so the true great American tooth was not very widely used.

Figure 20(a)   The vehicle developed for hauling logs out of deep wood-

Figure 21   Timber transport

land for loading. The nib, neb or bob was an improved version of the older 'pair o' wheels', shown beneath it. The neb was introduced about the middle of the nineteenth century, and had large wheels mounted on a heavy curved axletree. Long shafts were fitted, and above the axletree in a pair of bearings was a heavy roller with a long spar set in the centre. This was pulled upwards by a simple winch or 'wink'. The log was suspended in chains beneath the axletree, the chains being attached to the roller. The log was raised at one end by hauling on the winch, then dragged out with the end suspended below the wheels.

Figure 20(b) The earlier 'pair o' wheels' consisted simply of a pair of heavy cart wheels on an axletree as in the later neb, but with no shafts or winch. Leverage to the log to lift it was applied partly by wooden levers inserted in the square holes in the axletree and partly by the eccentric of the axles when the pull of the horses was applied. In some ways it was more useful than the neb, since it could operate in more confined spaces.

Figures 21(a), (b) and (c) Some of the waggons used for transporting timber from the woods to the yards. These were bolster waggons, more popularly known as tugs. They have their modern parallel in the heavy motor vehicles used today. There were various designs, mostly of a regional nature, but the main essentials were two heavy bolsters over the axles. The rear axle, complete with its wheels, could be moved along a stout longitudinal beam and secured at the desired position with an iron pin. The front axle and bolster were bolted and bracketed to the front end of the beam. Loading was done without the horses in, their power being used to load the waggon. Two stout poles were laid at an angle between the tops of the wheels on the side on which the log lay and the log, which was parallel to the waggon. The poles were lashed to the tops of the wheels to stop them from slipping, and two chains were laid out, from the tops of the bolsters, under the log and back over the top of the waggon to the horses, which were divided into two teams. The horses hauled the log up into place on the waggon, pulling at right angles to the vehicle. Chains were used to hold the load in preference to rope, and teams of eight or more horses were used to haul the waggons out. As far as possible dry conditions were chosen for moving the logs.

Figures 22 I (a) and (b) Tow dogs, ring pins or 'scor' pins were used for forming rafts and securing floating logs in the log ponds.

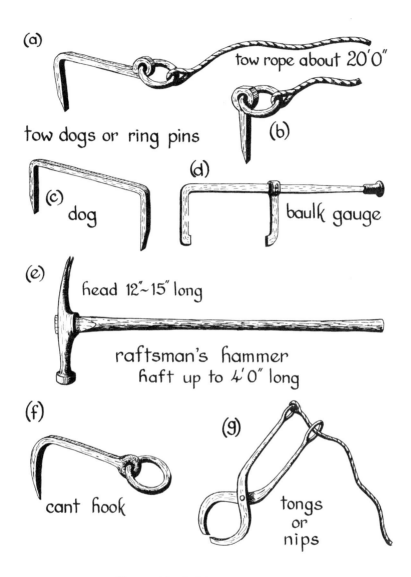

(a)

tow rope about 20'0"

tow dogs or ring pins

(b)

(c) dog

(d) baulk gauge

(e) head 12"~15" long

raftsman's hammer
haft up to 4'0" long

(f) cant hook

(g) tongs
or
nips

Figure 22   I Timber handling

Figure 22 I (c)   The usual form of iron dog used for fastening baulks together, building slipways, cradles and for other jobs around the ship and timber yards. These could be any size that might be needed.

Figure 22 I (d)   A baulk gauge, for measuring the size of squared baulk timbers. Much of the imported timber came in already squared, which made shipping much easier. Loads were often off-loaded at the mouths of rivers, especially on the East Coast, and sorted into rafts destined for different yards up the river. The gauge was used to check that the right sizes went to the right rafts.

Figure 22 I (e)   A raftsman's hammer from the East Coast used in making up the rafts. Dogs and tow rings were hammered in with this, and the long claw facilitated their removal.

Figure 22 I (f)   The usual form of cant hook used in shipyards and elsewhere for moving logs about the yard. Sometimes a rope was attached to the ring.

Figure 22 I (g)   Tongs or nips used for handling planks or poles around the yard. Hauling on the rope tightened the grip.

Figure 22 II (h)   This raft bridle or shackle consists of a short length of chain and two pins. The chain was linked through a hole in the wider of the two pins, and secured by a second pin with a flattish head driven through the other end link. One of the two pins, the wider one, was usually chisel-pointed.

Figures 22 II (i) and (j)   Two forms of cant poles used in working the log ponds and for turning logs. The first is the older, with the hook adjustable on a bolt through the pole. The second, a slightly later model, was limited in that no one pole could cope with the range of sizes, and several sizes were needed to handle all likely diameters of timber.

Figure 22 II (k)   The pike-pointed cant pole, sometimes called a peavey, was used extensively in Canada and elsewhere in handling logs on the rivers. They were also used in mast ponds in Britain about the middle of the nineteenth century, and perhaps earlier.

Figure 23 I (a)   This was probably the commonest form of pitsaw. Basically the pitsaw consisted of the blade, the tiller and the box. The saw itself cut only on the downstroke, the power being provided by the pitman working below the log. The top handle and its stem were known as the tiller, and using this the top sawyer steered the saw to his line. The lower handle was known as the box, and this was easily detachable to

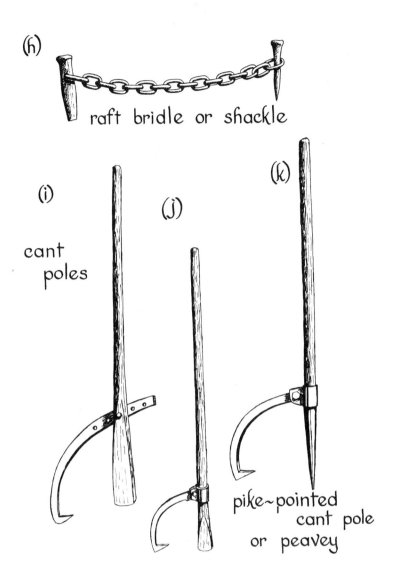

(h)

raft bridle or shackle

(i)

cant
poles

(j)

(k)

pike~pointed
cant pole
or peavey

Figure 22   II Timber handling

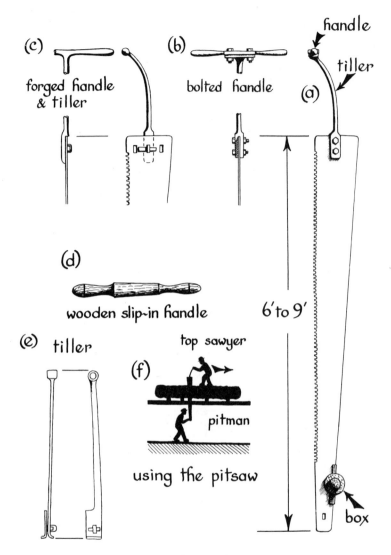

(c) forged handle & tiller

(b) bolted handle

(a) handle tiller

(d) wooden slip-in handle

(e) tiller

(f) top sawyer

pitman

using the pitsaw

6' to 9'

box

Figure 23 I Pitsaws

allow the saw to be inserted or withdrawn from the cut whenever required. Although virtually extinct in Britain, this form of saw was still made and shown in saw manufacturers' catalogues for years after World War II, as it was being made for export to countries like Africa, India and Pakistan for use in areas where power was not available.

Figures 23 I (b), (c), (d) and (e)   Various forms of tiller, handle and fastening. There were probably several other types.

Figure 23 I (f)   This illustrates the use of the pitsaw in silhouette. The top sawyer walked backwards along the top of the log, pulling the saw upwards and steering it on its downward cutting stroke. The pitman walked forwards, pulling the saw downwards. The saw edge was away from him, so that not so much sawdust fell directly on him as might be expected.

Figure 23 II (g)   A variation of the pitsaw known as a ribsaw. This was shorter than the very long pitsaws, very narrow, but fitted with the same type of tiller and box. It was almost exclusively a shipyard saw, as far as I can ascertain. The ribsaw was used on the pit for cutting the curves of the frames. The most skilful sawyers could almost work miracles with this saw. A West Country shipwright who had worked for many years in Falmouth once told me that he had known an old shipwright in the Falmouth yards who could remember using the ribsaw. He told how the frames were not just sawn out, but bevelled at the same time. My informant, having a pretty thorough knowledge of his craft since the 1920s, was very sceptical. Thinking of the hours he had spent dubbing down the frames with an adze, he asked how close the bevels could be cut. The answer was short and to the point : 'To the thickness of a pencil line'. The bevel on a frame varies from end to end; if this anecdote is true, it speaks volumes for the skills that have already gone.

Figures 23 II (h), (i), (j) and (k)   Various types of box used on pit-saws. The one generally favoured in the shipyards seems to have been (k), and (j) was more often found in rural workshops. Both these are the simpler and probably the older forms. The type in (h) is of the same period as the crosscut saw plate handles.

Figure 23 II (l)   The usual tooth outline of the pitsaws.

Figure 24(a)   A typical sawpit in use. The log is supported over the pit on beams, with wedges to steady it, and was probably dogged down as well. As the sawing progressed the beams were slid out and re-inserted behind the saw. A wedge was inserted in the sawcut to keep it open and

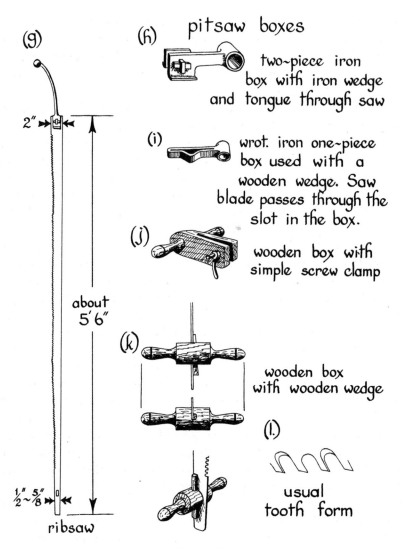

(g)

(h) pitsaw boxes

two-piece iron box with iron wedge and tongue through saw

2″

(i) wrot. iron one-piece box used with a wooden wedge. Saw blade passes through the slot in the box.

(j) wooden box with simple screw clamp

about 5′ 6″

(k) wooden box with wooden wedge

(l.) usual tooth form

½″ ~ ⅝″

ribsaw

Figure 23   II Pitsaws

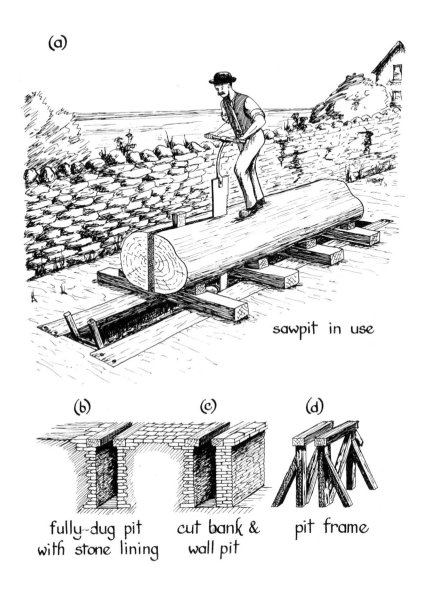

(a)

sawpit in use

(b)

fully-dug pit
with stone lining

(c)

cut bank &
wall pit

(d)

pit frame

Figure 24   The sawpit

bow or turning saws

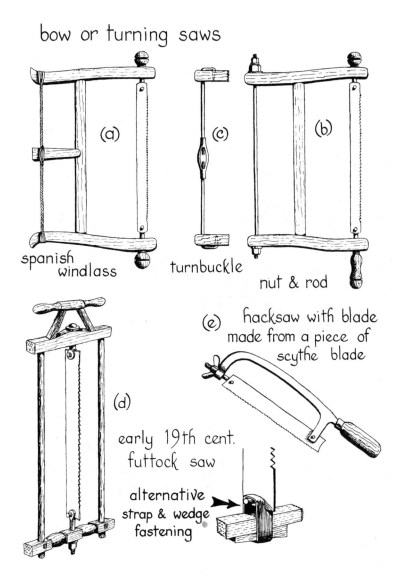

(a)

spanish windlass

(c)

turnbuckle

(b)

nut & rod

(d)

early 19th cent. futtock saw

alternative strap & wedge fastening

(e) hacksaw with blade made from a piece of scythe blade

Figure 25   Frame saws

prevent the saw from binding. In this case I have shown a ladder as access to the pit, but some pits had steps built into them.

Figures 24(b), (c) and (d) Various forms of the sawpit. The frame, in (d), was not much favoured owing to the difficulties involved in handling logs onto the top and moving them about once there. The stone-lined types had wooden kerbs built into them to close the gap at the top, into which iron dogs could be driven. Temporary pits were normally lined with planking or shuttering.

Figures 25(a), (b) and (c) Bow or turning saws showing various ways of tensioning the blade. The type used today is generally a small saw compared with those found in the shipyards, which might be as much as three feet long on the sawblade.

Figure 25(d) A futtock saw, which does not seem to have been used much since the early nineteenth century. In order to show the method of fastening clearly I have exaggerated the width of the blade, which was rarely over two inches. This saw was used for cutting out the short curved timbers known as futtocks which went into the construction of compound frames. It is obviously related to the Continental frame saw shown in Figure 18(d), but in this case the frame is there to support and tension a rather narrow blade used almost as a turning saw. I think the type was superseded in shipyards by the ribsaw, which could be used on the pit, whereas this type needed a frame, or trestle system. It is my belief that the Continental use of a frame was connected with the use of pull saws—a hangover from the use of soft metals or saws, which needed support.

Figure 25(e) A hacksaw used for cutting lengths of copper for keel and deadwood bolts. Blades suitable for cutting metal were not produced until the second half of the nineteenth century, and this meant some improvisation. The blacksmith could be relied upon to cut most metals either hot or cold, but the saw produced a neater edge with less trouble. Pieces of old scythe blade were often pressed into service as saw blades, or the blacksmith might be prevailed upon to produce a carbon steel blade by forging iron in a charcoal fire or on an oak anvil. It was a longish process, however, and there was no sure way of controlling the quality of the result.

Figures 26(a), (b) and (c) Three of the methods of driving a sawmill by horse-gin. These were operated from overhead, much in the way that

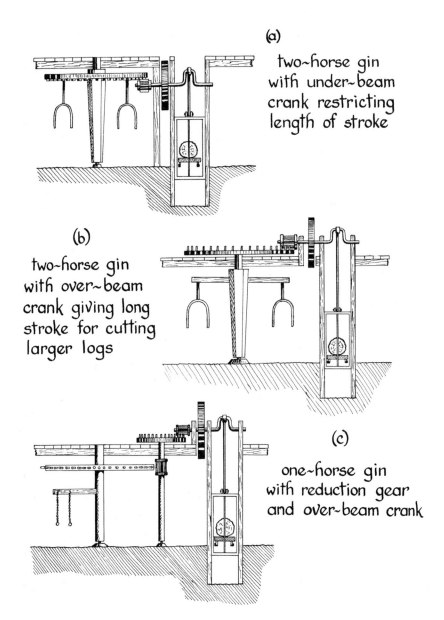

(a)

two-horse gin
with under-beam
crank restricting
length of stroke

(b)

two-horse gin
with over-beam
crank giving long
stroke for cutting
larger logs

(c)

one-horse gin
with reduction gear
and over-beam crank

Figure 26   Sawmills driven by horse-gins

a windmill might be used, and the system is more or less the same as that used on farms for cider pounds and for threshing. The gears were made by millwrights to the same standards used on windmills and watermills, using hornbeam and apple wood.

Large saws were sharpened by strapping the saw blade to a bench and filing the teeth. For small teeth the usual triangular or 'three-square' file was used, but for larger teeth a flat file was more suitable. The gullet was deepened with a round or rat-tail file. The set of the teeth to either side of the centre line of the saw was done by bending them with a saw set, which was a flat plate with a simple handle—sometimes all in one with the metal plate—with a series of slots of different widths cut in round the edges to fit differing gauges of saw.

The shipwright in his normal work used all the saws used by carpenters, just as much as any other trade. Ripsaws, hand crosscuts and tenon saws in various sizes were used, and in some yards were found mitre saws working in guides, exactly the same as those used today by professional picture framers. Keyhole and other piercing saws can also be found in some old craftsmen's tool boxes. The larger tools such as pitsaws were usually the property of the shipyard proprietor, but the shipwright was expected to supply his own hand tools.

4

THE SHIPWRIGHT

The trade of shipwright in a smaller shipyard often involved work which other trades might do in larger yards. I have already mentioned working on the sawpit and making masts and spars, and shipwrights were frequently called on to help riggers, sailmakers and in the outfitting work generally. In addition the master and often a foreman shipwright would be responsible for the entire design as well as the construction of a ship. The trade of caulker, in the days when ships were built entirely of wood, was sometimes regarded as one on its own, but strictly caulking was the domain of the shipwright. With the rise of iron and steel ship-building, caulking changed from rolling oakum and pouring pitch to burring over plate edges and trimming rivet heads, and the caulker became one of the steelworking tradesmen in his own right.

Methods of shipbuilding, although basically the same, had variants in different parts of the country. It would, however, be useful to outline the general method used in the smaller shipyards in order to put the tools involved in their proper places. This can only be a bare outline, for the whole task is a science of its own.

On being approached by a prospective client, the shipwright established just what was needed—the type of vessel, its purpose, its size and the qualities it was hoped to achieve. From this, perhaps assisted by the knowledge of an existing ship the client might admire, the master shipwright or his foreman carved a wooden half-model of the proposed hull. This would be discussed with the customer, altered if necessary, and eventually a contract might be agreed. From the model the customer would usually be able to see what sort of vessel he was getting, for he would be a practical seaman, most probably, with nearly as much knowledge of how a hull would perform as the shipwright. He would know, from his own experience, if the model needed more lift in the bows or afterbody, if the heel was deep enough, or whether he could

98

John Cann of Harwich with a batten-and-frame model of a Harwich
bawley, about 1898

safely ground her to discharge cargo without too much listing. The model
had the advantage that it presented the facts to a customer who in all
likelihood would be unable to understand a draughtsman's plan. In fact
drawings or plans were very little used in the old yards, and the whole
of the ship was built from the model. Although plans were used by the
naval dockyards from early on, the smaller yards did not make use of
them until the end of the nineteenth century. Wooden half-models were

used in the building of wooden ships. Such models were used in the building of metal ships solely for the purpose of measuring shell plating, as they still are, to some extent. As recently as 1948 a small British motor fishing vessel was built in a Brixham shipyard using a half-model, for wooden construction, and quite possibly the practice still exists. The mental ability to visualise a full hull form from a drawing was restricted in the early days to those few masters who possessed all the 'mysteries' of their craft, and the man who had grown up and learnt his trade in one of the smaller yards was completely lost. Sail plans were used, as this was the easiest way to work out masting, rigging and sails, but again this was not universal.

The lines of the approved model were lifted off and translated into terms of the full-size ship in the mould loft. I have already outlined the use of the mould loft and scrieve board, and there were various ways of lifting the lines, depending on the type of model and the practice of the particular yard. The battens or splines used to produce the curves on the mould loft floor were at one time made of ash. However, just before 1890 it was found that hickory, introduced as a substitute during a shortage of long ash, produced a far superior even curve, and it was widely adopted. The moulds, patterns or templates produced in the mould loft were passed to the shipwrights and sawyers for selection and cutting of the appropriate timbers.

Most of the cutting was done on the sawpit, but some timbers were partly or wholly cut out by axe. Masts and spars were always 'blocked out' by axe, and it was also used for certain work on the stem, stern and keel. The next stage was to lay the keel on the keel blocks and raise the stem and stern posts. Then the frames were set up on the keel. Battens were run round the hull to hold the frames fair, and to aid in judging the bevel of each frame. Then the bevels were dubbed on with the adze. The stem and stern deadwoods were fitted and the rabbet cut to receive the planking. Deck beams were fitted between the frames, and the shelf and various carlings and framing to the decks were fastened into place. Planking started from the keel upwards, and after all was fastened securely the hull was faired off by dubbing down with the adze. Decks were laid, and any deck fittings, hatches and so on fitted into place. The whole vessel was then caulked, by which time she would be pretty well ready for launching. That, very briefly, and omitting perhaps most of the story, was how a wooden ship was built.

100

THE FIGURES

Figures 27(a), (b) and (c) The three most commonly used types of half-model. The first is the block model, made either from a solid block of wood or from several layers of plank firmly joined together. This could be dealt with in the mould loft in various ways in order to take off the

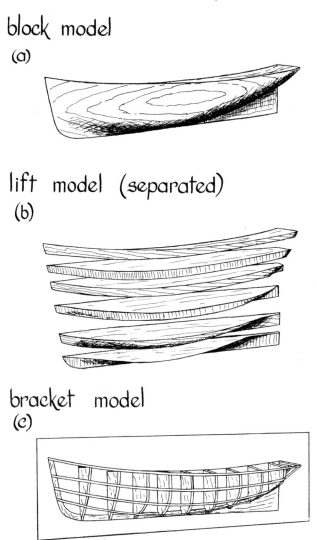

block model
(a)

lift model (separated)
(b)

bracket model
(c)

Figure 27   Shipbuilder's half-models

lines. The most common seems to have been the use of a bent lead wire following the curve, which was then drawn down and scaled up. Another way was to saw through the model to the backboard at fixed stations throughout its length—the same stations as used with the lead wire— at right angles to the keel. A sliver of wood shaving on which to draw the complete half-section was slipped into each sawcut and the section drawn on it. These were then drawn out and scaled up. The lift model in (b) was built from planks of even thickness to correspond with the scale of the model, so that each layer, when taken apart, represented what are known as waterlines throughout the hull. Lines drawn at the various stations on the back of the model—no backboard in this case—were squared across the top of each layer, and the resulting series of measurements could be directly scaled up and drawn full size. The rather similar bracket model was generally used for larger vessels owing to the great weight of a solid model. In this case the wooden bulkheads or moulds on which the model was based were placed at the various stations throughout its length, and measurements from the back to the front edge gave the same information as with the lift model.

Figure 28(a) A scrieve hook, which was used for cutting in the lines on a scrieve board.

Figure 28(b) Another version of the scrieve hook, made from an old file. So many tools were homemade in this kind of way that it is almost impossible to give a really representative example of many of them.

Figure 28(c) A scribing knife also used on scrieve boards and in the mould loft. Again it was usually either homemade—an old table knife was ideal—or adapted from some other tool. Its main use was the correction of errors in the scribed lines.

Figure 28(d) A pair of sweeps, the loftsman's compasses, which were used to draw chalk circles and curves. There was a limit to the usable size of sweeps when working full size, and this called for other measures.

Figure 28(e) A pair of trammel heads, used on a long beam for the larger sweeps and curves for which the normal sweeps were inadequate. French chalk in stick form was used a lot for this work. Straight lines were drawn by using a chalk line stretched between two nails and plucked in the centre. Provided that the line had been well chalked and the 'ping' of the line was true, this gave a fine, straight line.

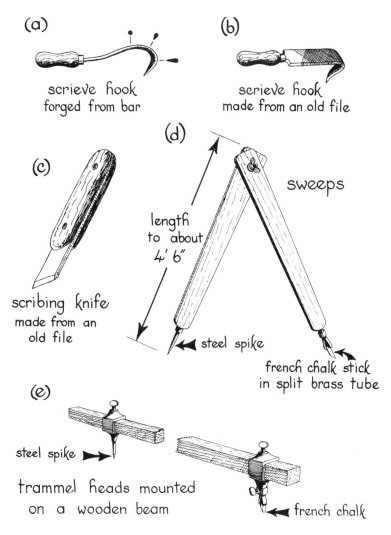

(a) scrieve hook
forged from bar

(b) scrieve hook
made from an old file

(c) scribing knife
made from an
old file

(d) length
to about
4' 6"

sweeps

steel spike

french chalk stick
in split brass tube

(e) steel spike ➤➤

trammel heads mounted
on a wooden beam

french chalk

Figure 28 Lofting or laying off

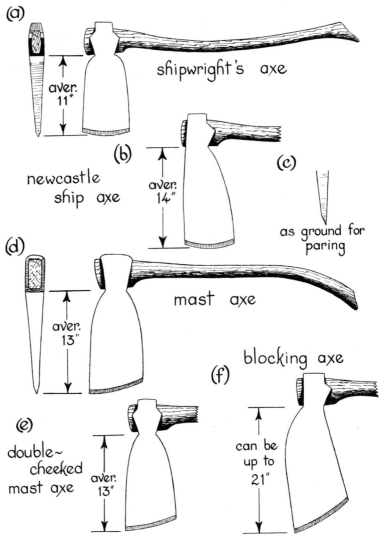

(a)

aver.
11"

shipwright's axe

newcastle
ship axe

(b)

aver.
14"

(c)

as ground for
paring

(d)

aver.
13"

mast axe

blocking axe

(f)

can be
up to
21"

(e)

double~
cheeked
mast axe

aver.
13"

Figure 29 I Axes

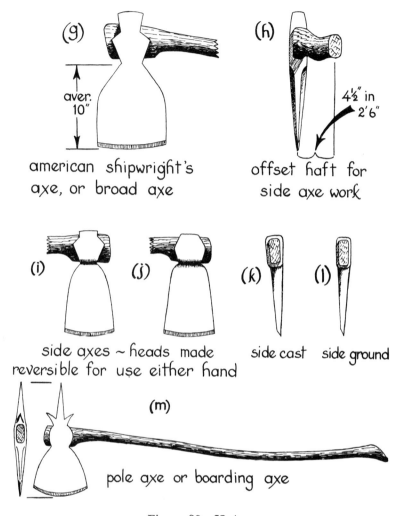

(g)

aver.
10"

american shipwright's
axe, or broad axe

(h)

4½" in
2'6"

offset haft for
side axe work

(i) (j)

side axes ~ heads made
reversible for use either hand

(k) (l)

side cast   side ground

(m)

pole axe or boarding axe

Figure 29   II Axes

Figure 29 I(a)   The shipwright's axe is a large-bladed version of the
Kent axe, with double cheeks and a long haft.
Figure 29 I (b)   A regional version known as the Newcastle ship axe,
which was more akin to the Kent felling axe but with a much deeper
blade.
Figure 29 I (c)   This illustrates how either of these axes could be
ground for paring or side cutting.

Figures 29 I (d) and (e)   Two forms of the mast axe, one being cheekless, the other double-cheeked. The hafts of mast axes were curved downwards at the end for some distance. This was to facilitate their use in blocking out, which was usually done below knee height.

Figure 29 I (f)   The great blocking axe, probably the largest type of axe produced for any trade, had a blade which could be as much as twenty-one inches deep. It needed a powerful man to wield such a tool. One such worked in the Falmouth yards during the 1920s and '30s, and I have been told that two men with the smaller sizes of axe worked on blocking out one side of a mast, while he worked the other side on his own. A fourth man was kept busy the whole time collecting the chips to give room for the three axemen to work. These axes had to be kept very sharp, and could be highly dangerous. Mast axes are still used in the vicinity of Lowestoft, among other places, though their use is declining fast. A story is told on that part of the East Coast of an unfortunate accident involving a mast axe. At one time children were allowed into the mast and spar shops when a mast was being 'sided' or blocked out, to collect the chips for kindling. On just such an occasion one of the shipwrights suddenly noticed a child's fingers, groping for chips, appear just where his axe was descending. He could not possibly stop the fall of the axe, but he could, and did, deflect its path, into his own leg. It was many months before that man could work again; he was lucky not to lose his leg. Needless to say, children were no longer allowed in the mast shops of the area.

Figure 29 II (g)   The American shipwright's axe, also known as the broad axe. The blade is not so deep as the usual shipwright's axe, but it is much wider. It is a double-cheeked axe with a heavy poll.

Figure 29 II (h)   This shows how the broad axe was hafted for side axe cutting. The haft had an offset of $4\frac{1}{2}$in in its length of 2ft 6ins

Figures 29 II (i), (j), (k) and (l)   Side axes with reversible heads so that they could be used either hand, and the two styles of head, the first cast with one face flat, the other with a normal face but the edge ground one-sided.

Figure 29 II (m)   This may look rather out of place, but the pole axe was used for handling timber, using the spike for moving logs. It was carried in large numbers on British naval vessels for general spar work and was also used as a boarding axe; large numbers of them were driven into the side of an enemy ship to form a ladder for boarding. Quite small

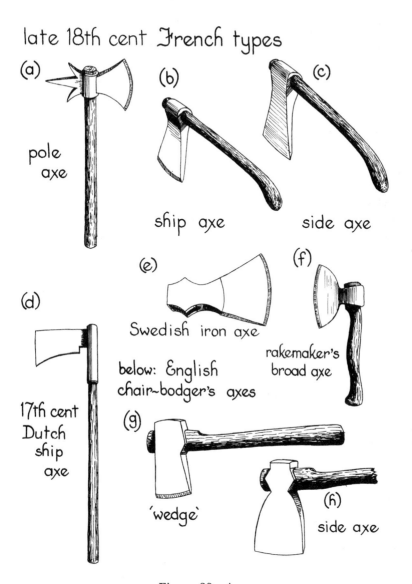

late 18th cent French types

(a)

pole
axe

(b)

ship axe

(c)

side axe

(d)

17th cent
Dutch
ship
axe

(e)

Swedish iron axe

below: English
chair~bodger's axes

(f)

rakemaker's
broad axe

(g)

'wedge'

(h)

side axe

Figure 30   Axes

ships might carry several dozen pole axes as part of their normal inventory.

Figure 30 A variety of earlier axes, some of which should not be confused with shipwright's axes.
Figures 30(a), (b) and (c) Late eighteenth-century types that, from the original illustrations, appear highly unsatisfactory in their hafting. These French axes are all shown with round eyes on a haft which does not seem even to be wedged.
Figure 30(d) A seventeenth-century Dutch ship axe, which had a socketed head rather like the earlier battle axes.
Figure 30(e) A Swedish iron axe head, which is akin to some of the English woodsman's axes and may have a common ancestor.
Figure 30(f) A strange little axe from the English countryside, a rake-maker's broad axe. It is not likely to be confused with any of the shipwright's axes, but may well turn up in any collection of tools from a coastal village.
Figures 30(g) and (h) Two axes that, if found without hafts, could well be confused with ship axes, though they are smaller. They are the English chair-bodger's 'wedge' and side axe, used extensively in the inland rural areas, usually in the woodlands themselves. Chair bodging was one of the coppice industries of rural England.

Another form of axe which I have not illustrated is the type referred to in the book *Southseaman*, by Weston Martyr, in his description of the building of a schooner in Nova Scotia in the 1920s. Unfortunately, in spite of his sketch and description, there is not enough to base a reliable drawing on, and no specific name seems to have been recorded for this great curved side axe. Instead of the usual side axe, this one seems to have had the whole head cast on a curve from the poll to the cutting edge, and I have not come across it anywhere else. It was employed to pare down the wood keel to fair in with the lead keel below it. The author's description of the task is a very fair one, and not in the least exaggerated, as anyone who has witnessed the old shipwrights working will confirm. These men swung their great axes with unerring accuracy, leaving a surface which hardly needed any further finishing.

Figure 31 I (a) The standard English shipwright's peg-poll adze, which perhaps personifies the shipwright's trade. The adze, or addice as it was once known, is not an easy tool to use, but once it has been mastered it

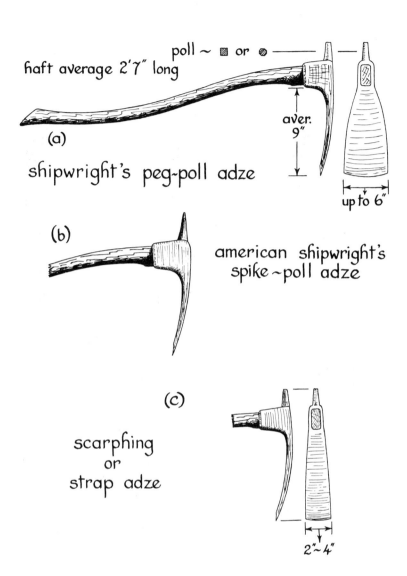

poll ~ ▨ or ◉ ————

haft average 2'7" long

(a)

shipwright's peg-poll adze

aver. 9"

up to 6"

(b)

american shipwright's
spike~poll adze

(c)

scarphing
or
strap adze

2"~4"

Figure 31   I Adzes

dubbing adzes

(d)

12"

**round-lipped
or 'spoon'**

(e)

**square-lipped
or 'box'**

(f)

6

**american
lipped adze**

slot adze

(g)

3"

5"

9"~10"

blade only

'spanish' adze

(h)

(i)

18th cent french adze

Figure 31   II Adzes

is magnificent. The double-curved haft, sometimes commented upon as unnecessary, gives the tool the essential balance without which the ship-wright would find it quite unmanageable for his type of work. The peg poll was used for driving spikes or bolts below the surface when dubbing down. This adze was made in four different sizes, the smaller three of which I have not been able to track down. No 4, the largest size, is common and was perhaps the most widely used. It is about six or seven inches wide on the blade. The size number is stamped on the inside flat of the blade. I have found smaller adzes, but generally they have been so worn down by sharpening that there has been insufficient to indicate the original width.

Figure 31 I (b)   The American shipwright's adze, with a spike poll. Why the sharp spike-poll I do not know, unless they used smaller fast-enings, but I would have thought it liable to slip on larger bolts and damage the planking. Apart from this it is similar to the previous adze.

Figure 31 I (c)   The scarphing adze, used for cutting long scarphs or joints in the timbers of keels, stems and masts, where the chisel or slice would not be man enough. Because of its long narrow blade it was some-times called a strap adze. The blade here was available in widths of from two to four inches.

Figure 31 II (d)   A rather rarer form of adze known as a dubbing adze; this example is called a round-lipped or 'spoon' adze. It was designed to cut across the grain when removing large amounts of timber. Two grooves were cut with this adze, one at each end of the desired area. Then the space between could be cleared out with the normal adze. In the right hands this could be a very rapid way to remove the waste from a large joint.

Figure 31 II (e)   Another pattern of the dubbing adze, known as a square-lipped or 'box' adze, and used for the same purpose.

Figure 31 II (f)   An American lipped adze, which was again used for the same task.

Figure 31 II (g)   A small adze that was not specifically designed for the shipwright. It was sold for use by all the woodworking trades in the nineteenth century under the name of slot adze. The cutting edge of the rather thin blade is about four inches wide, the other measurements are shown on the drawing. These were taken from the example in Brixham Museum, which came from a shipwright's tool box, but the Museum is constantly being told that it is a cooper's adze. This is an example of a tool being used by several trades and misinterpreted. It is a very handy tool, very like the adze from Abydos in Figure 5 I (d), and a style continued through the French design in Figure 31 II (i). The blade was held by a wooden wedge and a stirrup-like strap in each case.

Figure 31 II (h)   A curious small adze which so far I have only been able to trace along the south-west coast of Britain, and even then it was not very common. It went by the name of 'Spanish' adze, perhaps being based on a small adze used on the coasts of Spain and Portugal, but I remain to be convinced that it was not an adaptation from the slot adze, using a haft based on a saw handle, for working in confined spaces. The West Country seamen had many contacts with the Portuguese and Spanish coasts, and it is quite possible that they had seen this tool used there and that some seagoing shipwrights brought the idea back with them; but the little evidence I have been able to gather shows that the blade, stirrup and wedge are almost always interchangeable with those of the slot adze, which suggests merely a haft adaptation.

Figure 31 II (i)   An eighteenth-century French adze of similar form to the slot adze, but with a much heavier cast blade. The shaping of the terminal point of the haft suggests affinities with the slot adze of nineteenth-century England.

Figure 32   These are other adzes used by various tradesmen other than the shipwright, and are included here for identification purposes.

Figure 32(a)   The carpenter's adze, showing two forms of poll. The carpenter's adze usually has a slightly flatter blade than the shipwright's, and the haft is generally straighter.

Figure 32(b)   The wheelwright's or wheeler's adze, which is more curved to fit the inside of the felloes (the sections that make up the rim of a wheel). The poll is a flat block.

Figure 32(c)   A cooper's adze, which was much more hammer-headed than the other adzes. The blade could be either plain or clawed for removing nails, etc.

Figure 32(d)   The platelayer's adze was devised during the nineteenth century for laying railway tracks. It was a heavy-headed adze with a very solid block poll. The carpenter's and the platelayer's adzes had long hafts, rather straighter than the shipwright's, but the wheelwright's and cooper's adzes were fitted with short, straight hafts more like a hammer shaft.

Figure 33(a)   The common claw hammer used by most carpenters,

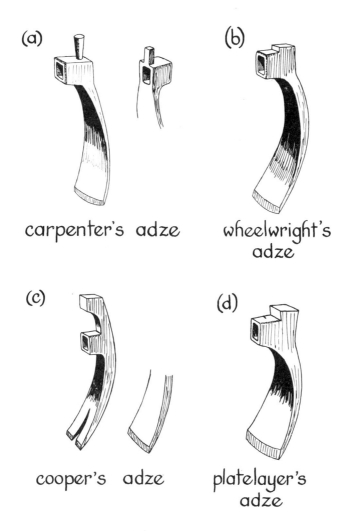

(a)

carpenter's adze

(b)

wheelwright's
adze

(c)

cooper's adze

(d)

platelayer's
adze

Figure 32   Adzes

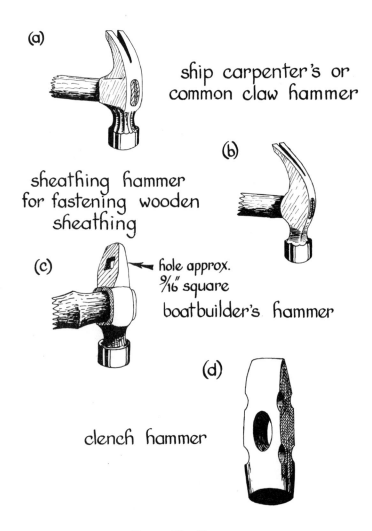

(a)

ship carpenter's or
common claw hammer

(b)

sheathing hammer
for fastening wooden
sheathing

(c)   hole approx.
        9/16" square

boatbuilder's hammer

(d)

clench hammer

Figure 33   Hammers

but sometimes sold under the name of a ship carpenter's claw hammer. Perhaps in this case it could be said to be rather larger than the usual carpenter's hammer, but they used some big ones too.

Figure 33(b)   A sheathing hammer used for applying wooden sheathing to a ship's hull or deck. The long claw enabled nails or spikes to be removed with less damage to the surrounding timber than with the short claw of the carpenter's hammer. Hammers were made and sold by their weight, and a variety of weights of each type were available.

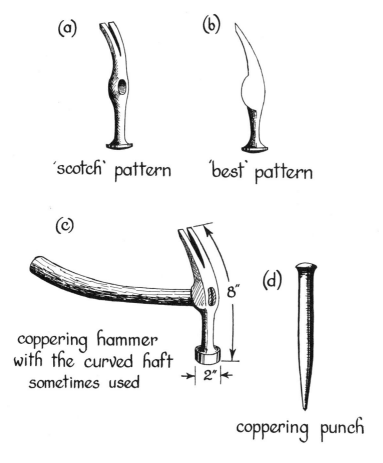

(a)

(b)

'scotch' pattern

'best' pattern

(c)

8″

(d)

coppering hammer
with the curved haft
sometimes used

2″

coppering punch

Figure 34 Coppering hammers

Figure 33(c) A boatbuilder's hammer found in a South Coast ship-yard. It had a cross pein with a square hole through it, which was reputed to be for breaking off the ends of copper nails used in clencher building before riveting them over the roves.

Figure 33(d) A commercial clench hammer for riveting copper nails. This was illustrated in Smith's Key of 1816, an early form of illustrated catalogue of things manufactured in Sheffield, for the use of commercial travellers.

Riveting of a clench-built boat was usually carried out by two men, one working inside, the other outside the hull. Holes for the nails were drilled, copper nails inserted, and a rove pushed and driven down over the end of the nail. The excess end of the nail was broken or clipped off, and riveted over the rove. It is on record, however, that one boatbuilder in Appledore, North Devon, was able to completely fasten a clencher boat on his own. His secret died with him, for he would never allow anyone to see him doing it. After his death his tools were examined by local shipwrights who found nothing out of the ordinary in them.

Figures 34(a) and (b)   A rather specialised hammer developed for fastening copper sheathing. Thin sheets of copper or yellow metal were fastened to the underwater body of sailing ships to protect them against various wood-boring pests such as the teredo or shipworm. The nails used were made of the same material. The sheathing hammer had a wide face to prevent damage to the sheets, and a long claw so that bent nails could be removed with the least damage.

Figure 34(c)   A sheathing hammer with the curved haft sometimes fitted for working on the inside curves of the stern. With many of these tools there were patterns known as 'Scotch' and either 'London' or 'best'. The Scotch patterns were usually rather rougher in finish compared with the London or best patterns, which often had ground faces on parts of the tools.

Figure 34(d)   A coppering punch, which was used for punching nail holes in the sheathing material. These punches were usually made up by a local blacksmith, or ground up from an old rat-tail file. The point was ground to a shallow 'v' to stop too deep a penetration.

Figure 35(a)   A riveting hammer, used more by sheet metal workers, but sometimes found among the shipwright's tools. Used for light copper nail riveting.

Figure 35(b)   A boilermaker's hammer, of the type made in 1816. It might well be found in a shipyard where early iron shipbuilding or engine building was carried out. It is not, however, a shipwright's tool as such.

Figures 35(c) and (d)   Forms of the seven-pound flogging hammer used for a variety of purposes in most shipyards. There is nothing particularly significant about them, and they were quite common and still are. The hafts were no more than those of slightly long hammers.

Figures 35(e), (f) and (g)   Common types of sledge hammer such might be found used today. The hafts are long, 2ft 6in or more.

Figure 36 I (a)   This illustrates the shipwright's or ship maul, which

116

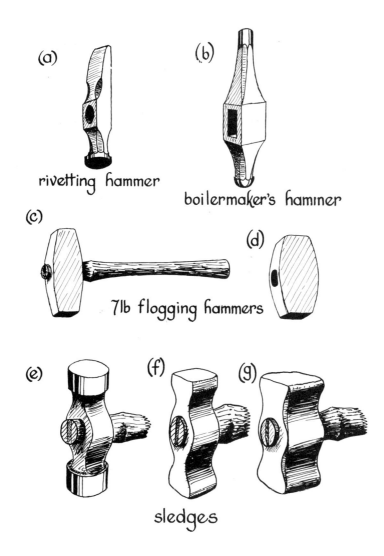

(a) rivetting hammer

(b) boilermaker's hammer

(c) (d) 7lb flogging hammers

(e) (f) (g) sledges

Figure 35   Hammers

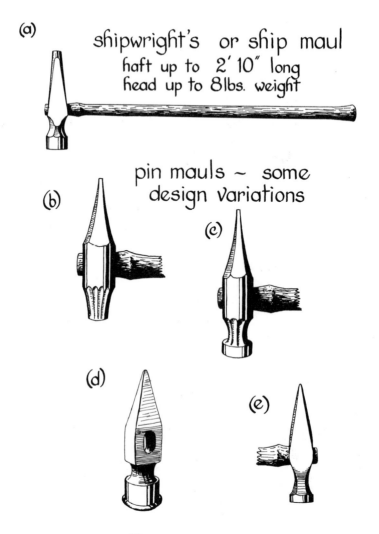

(a)

shipwright's or ship maul
haft up to 2' 10" long
head up to 8 lbs. weight

pin mauls ~ some
design variations

(b)

(c)

(d)

(e)

Figure 36 I Mauls

was the standard heavy hammer for ship work. It was made in various sizes up to eight pounds, with a haft up to 2ft 10in long. The peg poll was, as with the adze, designed for knocking down bolts and spikes.

Figures 36 I (b), (c), (d) and (e) Some of the various designs of the form of maul known as a pin maul. The pin maul had a finer point to the poll, which might be rounded, squared or octagonal.

118

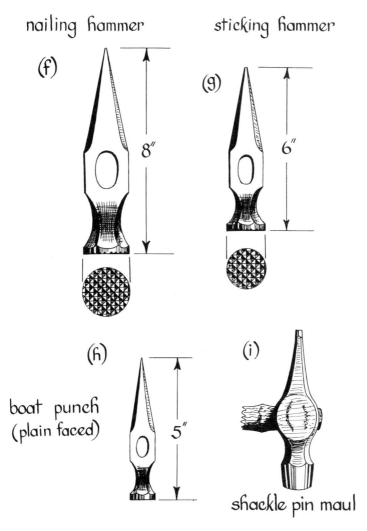

nailing hammer

(f)

8"

sticking hammer

(g)

6"

(h)

boat punch
(plain faced)

5"

(i)

shackle pin maul

Figure 36   II Mauls

Figure 36 II (f)   A variety of maul known as a nailing hammer. This is one of the tools illustrated in Smith's Key of 1816, as are the next two. In this case the face was chequered. The size shown here, eight inches high, was the nailing hammer; the smaller sizes went under different names.

Figure 36 II (g)   This shows the smaller version, six inches high, also with a chequered face, and shown in the 1816 list as a sticking hammer.

Figure 36 II (h)   The last of the 1816 mauls, only five inches high, much lighter, with a plain face and named as a boat punch.

All three of these—Figures 36 II (f), (g) and (h)—seem to have become obsolete during the first half of the nineteenth century, and I know of no examples which have survived.

Figure 36 II (i)   A shackle pin maul, which is not a shipwright's but a rigger's tool. I have included it among the mauls because it fits in well with the other tools, and is in any case a maritime tool. The spike was used for knocking out shackle pins, as the name implies. Sometimes these are found lying about in shipyards; they were often kept handy near chain moorings on a quayside.

Figures 37 (a) and (b)   Chisels with a solid forged shank and cap, with no wooden parts at all, known as boat or bargebuilder's chisels. For some unknown reason the bargebuilders on the Thames seemed to prefer this type. The caps might be rough, as in (b), or the better-finished type shown in (a).

Figures 37(c) and (d)   The wooden-handled type of chisel preferred by shipwrights, and known as the ship or shipwright's chisel. Figure 37(c) shows a socketed chisel with a plain rounded top for hand use. The type shown in (d) is also socketed, but with an iron-bound top for driving. Most of the shipwright's chisels were socketed types.

Figure 37(e)   The standard mortice chisel, which was used as much in shipwrightry as any other woodworking trade, though the shipwright's might be rather heavier.

Figure 37(f)   A tanged chisel, which was not very often used by the shipwright. It was termed a hand chisel, and was reserved for comparatively light work.

Figure 37(g)   The ship or shipwright's slice or slick. This chisel type of tool was cranked to enable it to be used on long cuts, with a slicing action, hence the English name of slice. It is usually found in widths of $3\frac{1}{2}$in and up, generally about 4in. A socketed type is shown, with an unusually short wooden handle in proportion to the metal parts. This is because most of these slices are of the order of 20–24in long. The wooden handle always appears not quite to seat down in the socket. This is because it was caulked in with a ring of cakum to absorb some of the shock. Very occasionally it is found with an iron-bound top.

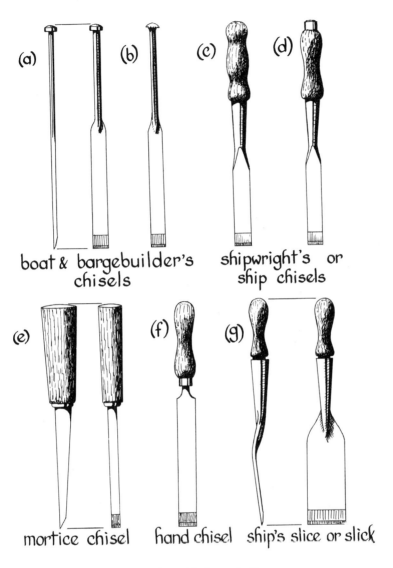

(a)

(b)

(c)

(d)

boat & bargebuilder's
chisels

shipwright's or
ship chisels

(e)

(f)

(g)

mortice chisel

hand chisel

ship's slice or slick

Figure 37   Chisels and slices

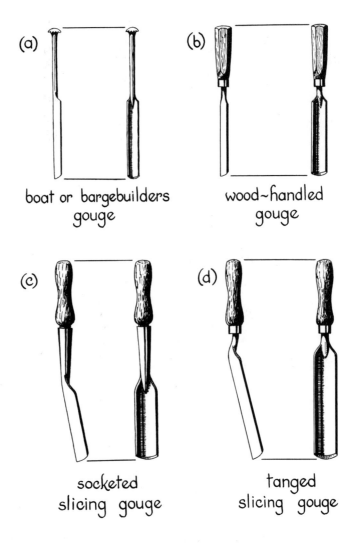

(a) boat or bargebuilders gouge

(b) wood-handled gouge

(c) socketed slicing gouge

(d) tanged slicing gouge

Figure 38   Gouges

Figure 38(a) The boat or bargebuilder's gouge, which, in common with the chisel, is iron-shanked.

Figure 38(b) The usual woodworker's gouge, found in most tool chests, and used for lighter work by the shipwright.

Figures 38(c) and (d) Two versions of the slicing gouge used by ship-wrights. The socketed type in (c) is the more common.

Figures 39 I and II A variety of tools used in caulking. The first task is to open the seam, if necessary, with 'reaming' or 'raming' irons. If old caulking is being renewed, the seams are first picked out with a rake or hoe. Oakum, picked from old rope (once a common task for convicts) is rolled or 'spun' between the palm of the hand and the knee into long strands. The strands are then driven into the seams with the caulking iron, and compressed or 'hardened down' with the 'making iron'. This presses the oakum below the surface of the seam, and it is then filled or 'payed up' with pitch. On ships sides the pitch is applied with a pitch mop. On decks a ladle is used. The various irons are driven with the caulking mallet, and the customary way was to caulk from left to right, and to 'make' from right to left. Experience was very necessary in making, because if the seam were too tight it could spring the seams and even shear off fastenings; too slack, the seam could leak.

Figure 39 I (a) A treenail iron, usually with a blunt edge about 1in wide. Used for splitting the ends of treenails for caulking. The method of fixing treenails (wooden pins used as fastenings) is shown in Figure 42.

Figure 39 I (b) A spike iron, also known as a sharp or butt iron (though there is another sharp iron which is quite different) it has a narrow blade, tapering to about $\frac{3}{4}$in, and is used for caulking in narrow spaces.

Figure 39 I (c) A sharp iron, with a flat edge, which is sharpened like a chisel. Used for cutting out old or unwanted oakum.

Figure 39 I (d) A caulking iron, or setting iron, or set iron. Various sizes between about $1\frac{3}{4}$–$2\frac{1}{2}$in, depending upon the extent to which it has been sharpened back. The fan-shaped blade can be either blunt or sharp. Used for caulking-in the oakum.

Figure 39 I (e) A bent iron, similar to the caulking iron in use, but a narrow iron usually flat across the edge. Cranked for getting into awkward corners when driving oakum in.

Figure 39 I (f) A making iron, a narrow type with a 1in-wide blade. Only one of several types of making irons.

Figures 39 I (g) and (h) Making irons of the type. also known as

123

caulking irons

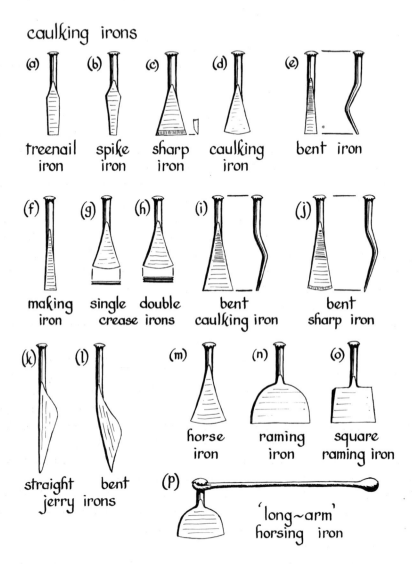

(a) treenail iron
(b) spike iron
(c) sharp iron
(d) caulking iron
(e) bent iron
(f) making iron
(g) single (h) double crease irons
(i) bent caulking iron
(j) bent sharp iron
(k) straight (l) bent jerry irons
(m) horse iron
(n) raming iron
(o) square raming iron
(p) 'long~arm' horsing iron

Figure 39 I Caulking tools

crease irons. These could have either a flat edge, as the previous type, or one, two or even three creases in the edge.

Figure 39 I (i)   A bent caulking iron, similar to the type shown in *Figure 39 I (e)* but with a wider fan-shaped blade.

Figure 39 I (j)   A bent sharp iron, used as the sharp iron in Figure 39 I (c), but bent for awkward places, and with a rounded edge.

Figures 39 I (k) and (l)   Jerry irons, longer than the usual irons, about 1ft long. Tapering from front to back to avoid jamming in the seam when driven along it, they were used for clearing out old seams. Various other names, such as hook rave, reaping iron, reefing iron, meeking or meaking iron and cleaning or clearing iron.

Figure 39 I (m)   A horse iron, a making iron of rather larger size than the usual irons. Used on thick planking. I believe this is known as a horsing or hausing iron, especially in the United States of America.

Figures 39 I (n) and (o)   Raming irons, also known as reaming, ream, deck or dumb irons, or as deck rives. About nine inches wide across the edge, in either square or semi-circular style. Used for opening up seams for caulking.

Figure 39 I (p)   A 'long-arm' horsing iron, a making iron of fairly large size, used by two men. Sometimes the iron has a loose bridle, which at one time was of twisted withy. Another version is reputed to have had the bridle and iron forged in one piece, but I have yet to find one.

Figure 39 II (q)   A caulking mallet, the pride and joy of many shipwrights, who will tell you that a well cared-for caulking mallet can halve the work to be done. The caulking mallet sings while it works, the note it makes when it strikes the iron being quite musical. The shipwrights liked to hear the singing of the mallet, and in some ports everyone tried to get a different note from his fellows. The mallet had a head made from either lignum vitae, beech or American oak of the kind known as 'live' oak, all very hard woods. The ends of the head were bound with tapering iron rings which were caulked on. These could be moved back as the mallet face wore down. The central boss had a tapered round hole for the haft, and was reinforced by two copper rivets. On either side of the haft hole, extending towards the ends, a slot was cut, usually with a round hole through the centre of the slot. These slots were the cause of the musical note, and the length of the slots and the number and size of the round holes tuned them. It has been said that if the slots were not there the noise made by a gang of shipwrights caulking would very soon deafen them.

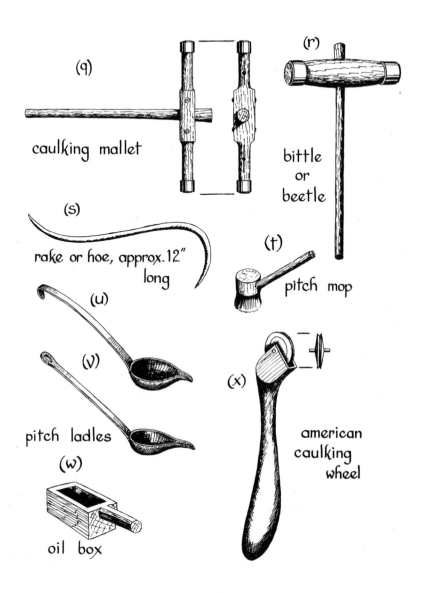

(q)

caulking mallet

(r)

bittle
or
beetle

(s)

rake or hoe, approx. 12″ long

(t)

pitch mop

(u)

(v)

pitch ladles

(w)

oil box

(x)

american caulking wheel

Figure 39 II Caulking tools

A team of caulkers habitually worked together, and in a small yard probably all the shipwrights would be called in on the job. A team like this might tune their mallets like a peal of bells, and working in rhythm could help them keep up a fast rate of work. It is said that the master shipwright in many of the yards could tell which of his shipwrights was slacking if his mallet did not fall at the right time.

In course of time the heads of the caulking mallets wore down on their faces too far to be of any further use for caulking. When this happened they were seldom discarded, usually being converted into beetles or 'bittles', or used by the shipwrights as chiselling mallets. The usual square-headed mallet used for chiselling by carpenters and joiners is seldom found in the shipwright's tool chest, being too small for the sizes of chisel usually used, but sometimes the little round mallet used for wood carving does turn up.

Figure 39 II (r) The beetle, bittle or caulking hammer, as distinct from the caulking mallet. It was used mainly for driving horsing irons or jerry irons and similar heavy work. The ends were iron-bound to prevent splitting.

Figure 39 II (s) A hoe or rake, usually made up locally from $\frac{1}{4}$in or $\frac{3}{8}$in round bar. It was used for raking out old oakum from seams.

Figure 39 II (t) The pitch mop was used for sealing seams on ship's sides with pitch. Although called a mop, it is actually a round, stiff-bristled brush head on a long handle.

Figures 39 II (u) and (v) Pitch ladles used for filling seams on decks with pitch. These had long spouts to aid and control the pouring, and prevent overspill as much as possible.

Figure 39 II (w) A simple oil box, cut from solid wood, and kept topped up with linseed oil. The caulking irons were dipped in the oil to prevent them sticking in the seams. Linseed and pitch are compatible, and the oil does not prevent the pitch sticking. Pitch was the original material used, but a caulking compound or marine glue which is based on pitch or bitumen is used today.

Figure 39 II (x) An American device for putting in the oakum before hardening down. For regular seams in long runs it could save a lot of time, though it would probably mean more hardening down. It is a fairly modern tool, thought to date from about 1930, not at all one of the traditional ones.

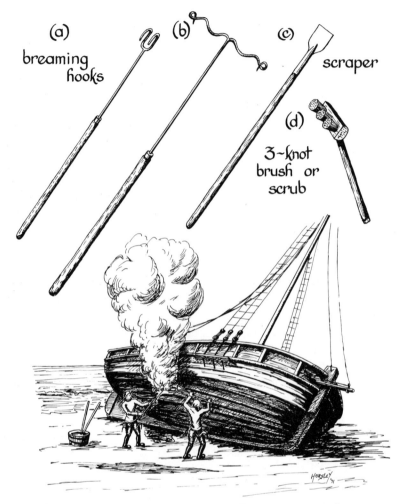

(a) breaming hooks

(b)

(c) scraper

(d) 3-knot brush or scrub

breaming a small sailing vessel
before graving or re-tarring

Figure 40   Breaming

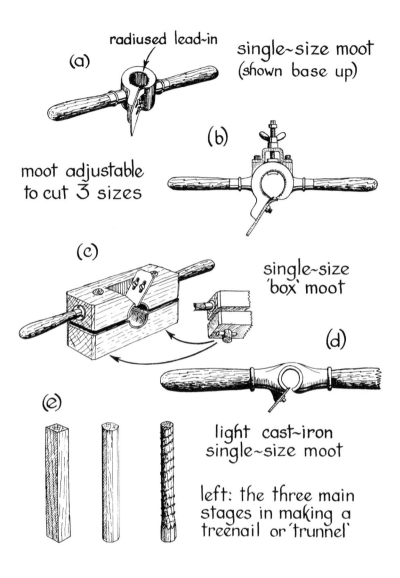

(a)

radiused lead-in

single-size moot (shown base up)

moot adjustable to cut 3 sizes

(b)

(c)

single-size 'box' moot

(d)

light cast-iron single-size moot

(e)

left: the three main stages in making a treenail or 'trunnel'

Figure 41   Moots, mutes or treenail makers

Figure 40 A vessel being breamed, a practice which seems to have died out by about the middle of the nineteenth century. It is a very old practice, involving careening the ship and burning off the old bottom coating, which was basically tar, then re-tarring it. The re-coating was termed graving, from the fact that at one time a concoction called 'graves' made from tallow and other substances was applied. It was from this that the term 'graving dock' originated. My sketch shows a small vessel of the early nineteenth century careened on a beach being breamed or burned off. One man uses the breaming hook, with its bundle of burning reeds or straw, burning away the tarring, while the second wields a scraper.

Figures 40(a) and (b) Breaming hooks, with long iron heads to keep the burning material away from the wooden handle. Reeds or straw seem to have been preferred as the 'bream'.

Figure 40(c) The type of scraper used for scraping off the soft remnants of the tar.

Figure 40(d) A typical three-knot scrub of the kind used for scrubbing down before re-tarring. The tarring itself might also be done with scrubs of the same kind.

The treenail, trennel or trunnel was one of the principal fastenings used in wooden shipbuilding. It was a stout wooden pin, usually oak, driven into a hole bored about one-eighth of an inch under the size of the treenail. The ends were then split and caulked or wedged.

Figure 41(a) A typical single-size moot, mute, treenail-maker, treenail plane, treenail rounder or rounding plane. These were some of the names given to the tool used for making treenails. For steadiness the tool needed to be fairly heavy, and in this case the central boss is of cast brass. It has a radiused lead-in, and a blade set into the side of it. The moot was turned round the roughly-shaped treenail to round it off.

Figure 41(b) A larger moot with an adjustable block in the side with marks for $1\frac{1}{2}$in, $1\frac{3}{4}$in and 2in diameter treenails.

Figure 41(c) A 'box' moot, suitable for only one size of treenail, made from heavy blocks of wood. Two wooden dowels of large diameter held the blocks together, and to some extent could be tightened by means of tapered wedges under the lower block. The hole for the treenail, cut half into each block, was lined with brass.

Figure 41(d) A lighter cast-iron moot, again in a single size, which I believe to be a later product than either the wooden or brass types. I

130

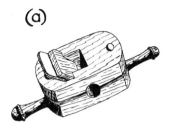

(a)

ladder~maker's
     stave block,

with one or two blades,
  usually curved

scythe snaith maker's
     stail engine,
usually two blades

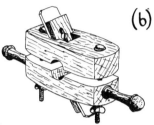

(b)

below: fixing treenails

outside: single split,
caulked with oakum

inside: cross split,
fitted with wedges

Figure 42 Tools like moots used by other trades

have also seen a cast iron moot in which the handles were cast in solid with the boss. This particular one was used in the little port of Salcombe, South Devon, and was probably a product of a local but very thriving foundry in the nearby town of Kingsbridge. The Lidstone Foundry made a range of items for the maritime trades, such as pump-handle windlasses, iron pumps, cast iron hawse pipes and deck manholes.

Figure 41(e)   The three main stages in making a treenail. The first stage is cleft out of oak, then roughly chopped off to an octagonal shape. Then the base was gripped in a vice and the moot brought into use. Although many of the treenails used were made in the shipyard, large numbers were bought ready-made. At Salcombe one of the shipwrights set himself up in a very nice small way of business making nothing but treenails for the local shipyards. He had plenty of work, and could always be making stock. His grand-daughter, now well into her seventies, recalls seeing the long rows of wooden 'soldiers' on the shelves and window-sills of her grandfather's workshop when she was very young.

Figures 42(a) and (b)   These are included as a warning that other trades used tools of a similar type. The ladder-maker's stave block, Figure 42(a), is one of them, but fortunately it usually has curved blades, which would be quite unsuitable for making treenails. The other example rejoices in the name of the scythe snaith maker's stail engine, and was used for rounding the hafts or snaithes of scythes. Most of these have two blades, one in each block, and may not have the brass or gunmetal liner usual in a wooden moot; the blades were fitted with wedges, while the moot had none.

Figure 42   Also shows the method of fastening treenails, which was done with the aid of the treenail iron. On the outside of the hull the treenail was given one split, then caulked with oakum. This called for great care, as over-caulking could split plank and frame. Inside the hull a cross-shaped split was made and fitted with wooden wedges.

Figure 43   Some of the different types of augers that have been used in shipbuilding over the past one and a half centuries or so. There were two types, the plain augers and the spiral augers, which all seem to derive from the auger devised by the Englishman Phineas Cooke about 1770, but not, apparently, very much favoured at its first introduction.

Figures 43(a), (b), (c), (d) and (e)   These are all versions of the oldest form of auger, basically the pod bit, which is sometimes known in

132

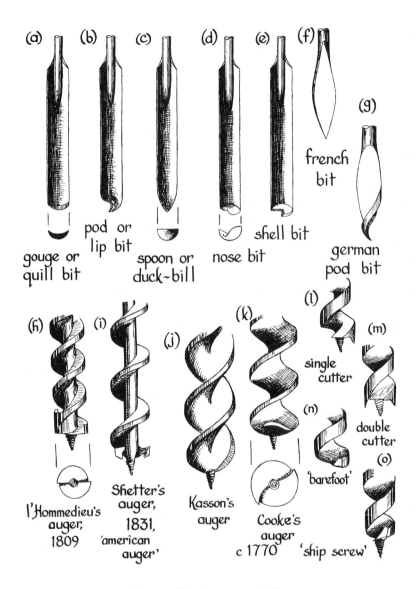

Figure 43 Augers and bits

its smaller sizes as a quill bit. The bit might or might not have a small lip or cutter at the end, and the form of the end seems to have given rise to various, though not universally used, names. Thus (a) could be a gouge or quill bit, (b) a lip bit, (c) a spoon or duckbill, (d) a nose bit, or (e) a shell bit. The shipwright used a variety of sizes of pod bit, and they were often preferred to the later spiral augers, reputedly being less likely to wander or run out in the wood, and not liable to bind in deep holes. The hafts of these augers were made in one piece with the bit, with a forged or cast-in eye for a simple slip-in handle. The hafts could be up to 12ft long in the larger sizes of auger, forged to about 1in or $1\frac{1}{4}$in square for most of the length. The general sizes, however, were rather smaller with hafts of 1–3ft, the bits being up to about $3\frac{1}{2}$in.

Figure 43(f)   A version of the diamond or French bit sometimes found used for light work or for starting holes for larger pod bits. It, too, is a very ancient form.

Figure 43(g)   An adaptation of the French bit with a twisted point to it; known as a German pod bit, it is no relative of the true pod bit. It is not commonly found among shipwrights' tools.

Figures 43(h), (i), (j), (k), (l), (m), (n) and (o)   All forms of the spiral auger. The first spiral auger is said to have been invented by one Lilley of Connecticut, USA, and later re-invented by Gurley of Mansfield, Connecticut, about 1800. However, Phineas Cooke invented his spiral auger in England about 1770, in the form shown in (k). Various patents were taken out in the United States for varying forms of spiral auger during the first third of the nineteenth century, such as Hoxie's patent of 1804, Hale's of 1807, and L'Hommedieu's of 1809, which is shown in (h). This was the type known as a 'solid centre' auger, in which the vanes are wrapped round a central core. Cooke's and the later Kasson's augers were of the open-centred forms, being basically flat bars twisted to shape. Shetter's auger of 1831, shown in (i), was another solid-centre auger which was very popular. It became known in Britain as an 'American' auger. There were about a dozen other US patents for augers between 1800 and 1834, with varying degrees of success. Gradually the form of the spiral auger developed into two basic forms other than open or solid centres—the single or the double cutter types. The single cutter was available in two or three types, but the variation was merely a matter of the design of the cutters themselves. Some had vertical knives as well as the horizontal ones, some did not. The single-cutter auger in (l) has an open centre, with both vertical knife and horizontal cutter. The type

134

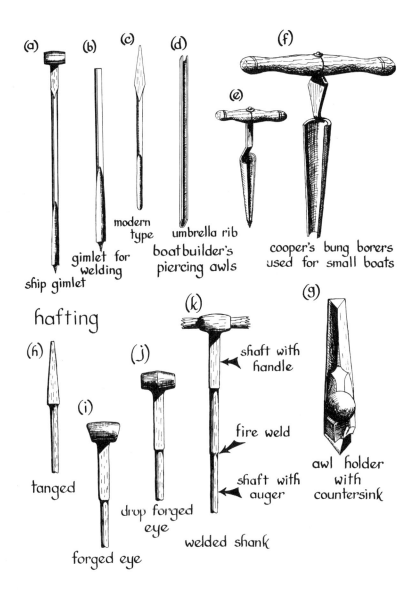

(a)

(b)

(c)

(d)

(f)

(e)

modern
type

ship gimlet

gimlet for
welding

umbrella rib
boatbuilder's
piercing awls

cooper's bung borers
used for small boats

hafting

(h)

(i)

(j)

(k)

(g)

shaft with
handle

fire weld

shaft with
auger

tanged

drop forged
eye

welded shank

awl holder
with
countersink

forged eye

Figure 44   Gimlets, awls, etc

known as a 'ship screw' auger, (c), has no vertical knife, while the 'barefoot' auger in (n) has neither vertical knife nor spiral lead-in. Because of the lack of a spiral lead-in, it was preferred by many ship-wrights who claimed that it was not diverted from a true hole by the lead-in following a wavy grain. This, of course, was the reason for the pod auger being so long a favourite. The auger in (m) is the double-cutter type with two vertical knives in addition to the normal horizontal cutters.

I have illustrated these augers in some detail because some of the early types of spiral auger are still to be found in old nineteenth-century shipyards. Also the shipwright had a habit of collecting a variety of tools which he could put to use in work other than straight shipbuilding. In many yards he was expected to do the joinery involved in constructing cabins and the cabin furniture, even in some cases down to finishing in French polish, if it was a 'classy' ship.

Figure 44(a)   The common ship gimlet, used for making holes up to about 1in in diameter. The hafts run up to about 3ft 6in long, and again have the eye for a slip-in handle.

Figure 44(b)   A gimlet head bought from the makers for welding on to an older haft. This was common practice with these rather long gimlets, which, due to the small diameter of the haft, had a habit of breaking off from time to time. The blacksmith was then called in to cut off what remained of the cutting edge and weld on a new shank.

Figure 44(c)   A boatbuilder's piercing awl, a modern style for use in a normal brace. The piercing awl was used for drilling holes in the planking of clench-built boats for riveting. The older version is shown in Figure 46.

Figure 44(d)   One of the boatbuilder's own home-made tools for the same purpose. A ground-down umbrella rib, usually fitted into a wooden stock, or directly into a simple boat sway or brace, and used as a piercing awl.

Figures 44 (e) and (f)   Two styles of the cooper's bung borer, which were adopted by boatbuilders for boring out the tapered bungholes used for draining water out of small boats. In later times a special brass plug-hole fitting with a screw-in brass bung or plug was often fitted in the more up-to-date yards.

Figure 44(g)   A combined awl holder and countersink that could be obtained to fit into a brace or sway. This held the awl bit with a screw

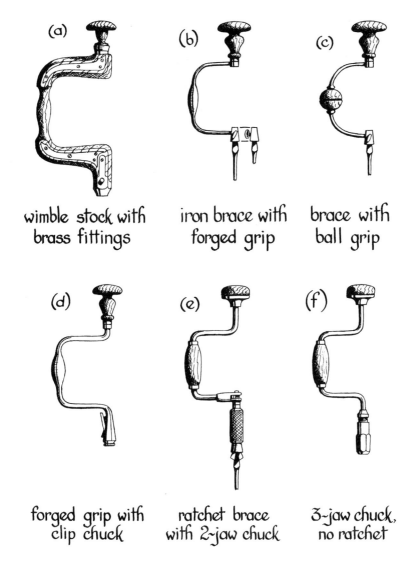

(a) wimble stock with brass fittings

(b) iron brace with forged grip

(c) brace with ball grip

(d) forged grip with clip chuck

(e) ratchet brace with 2-jaw chuck

(f) 3-jaw chuck, no ratchet

Figure 45   Braces

clamp arrangement, and allowed holes to be drilled and countersunk at the same time.

Figures 44(h), (i), (j) and (k)   Various ways of hafting augers and gimlets. The tanged style in (h) is the older style, which was embedded in a wooden cross handle and the end perhaps riveted over. The earlier handle eye was hand forged, rather like that in (i), and later drop forged versions, such as (j), came on the market. The whole layout, also showing the use of a welded cutting head, is in (k).

Figure 45(a)   A common form of the shipwright's wimble stock—as he frequently called his brace. The tool is in many respects similar to those used by all other woodworkers. In fact these were often made up by the craftsmen themselves, and they come in many forms. The one I have illustrated came from a shipwright, and is made of oak, with brass fittings. The brass fittings were sold in sets for this purpose. The chuck was a simple socket with a spring device to hold the bit in place. This was released by the button on the side.

Figures 45(b), (c) and (d)   Some of the stages of development from the wooden stock to the iron brace. The form in (b) had a forged iron bulb for a grip, and the bit was retained with a screw set in the side of the tapered chuck. The next, (c), is similar, but the bulb has been replaced with a revolving wooden ball. In (d) the iron bulb is retained but the chuck is now fitted with a clip device. In each case the top is a revolving boss, even on the wooden wimble stock.

Figures 45(e) and (f)   Two more modern versions, though neither is quite up to the modern style of brace. The version shown in (e) has a ratchet to the chuck, which itself is only a two-jaw type, closed by revolving the barrel. That in (f) has no ratchet, but a three-jaw chuck closed by revolving the barrel. Both types have revolving barrel-type hand grips.

Figure 46(a)   A dowelling auger that was used for sinking holes over those made for bolts, in which were inserted small cross-grained dowels. This was normally done on decks. The dowel plugs might be up to two inches across, the depth being a little less than the diameter. They were driven into place, sometimes with a little pitch or marine glue under them. This left the deck clear of bolt heads. This auger was designed to slip into the hole drilled for the bolt and cut the dowel recess in line with the bolt.

Figure 46(b)   A similar tool, though known as a counterbore. In this

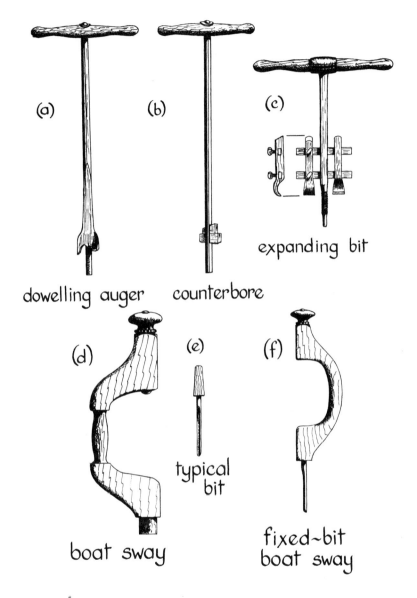

(a)

(b)

(c)

expanding bit

dowelling auger   counterbore

(d)

(e)

(f)

typical
bit

boat sway

fixed~bit
boat sway

Figure 46   Counterbores, etc

case the size of dowel hole was adjustable, the bit being simply a straight cutter with alternative bevels held in place by a steel wedge.

Figure 46(c) A third form of what is basically the same kind of tool, but here the cutters are set in a vertical position and are fully adjustable to the outer ends of a pair of bars set across the shank. The lower part of the shank had a fine spiral thread on it to pull the cutters into play. This tool was not generally used for fitting dowels, being rather too large over the cut, but for sinking recesses in the deck to take the cast covers at the heads of filler pipes, deck glands and the like.

Figure 46(d) The boatbuilder's version of the wimble stock, known as a boat sway. The head is a revolving one, the rest is one piece of wood, with a tapered socket to take the bit.

Figure 46(e) The type of bit used in the boat sway, which was fitted into a small wooden block. This was tapered to fit the socket of the sway. The umbrella-rib piercing awl shown in Figure 44(d) was fitted in this way, when it was not used in a fixed-bit sway.

Figure 46(f) A fixed-bit sway, in which the bit was permanently set in the end. A range of these were kept by the boatbuilder, one for each size of bit. Again these were generally home-made, the revolving top being about the only refinement of any kind above the very simplest and most primitive drill of the brace type. The tops were used again and again on new stocks as the older ones became useless or cracked.

Figure 47(a) A rather rare form of patent breast drill, the 'Glasgow' patent of 1907. In its way this is an early form of power drill, operated by a chain pulling a drum round, and returned on the free side of the ratchet by a spring. The breast-plate was a box for drills with a hinged lid opening both sides of the centre line. The chuck was of the split-collet type closed by a knurled barrel or nut.

Figure 47(b) A drill feed device for converting the power of a hand brace to drill through iron or steel sections. The feed was chucked in the brace in place of the drill, then the drill chucked into the feed's own chuck. The chain was led round the section being drilled and back through a slot in a cast piece which ran on two steel bars and the centre pole, which was threaded. Each turn of the drill knocked a small sprocket round one place, the other side of the sprocket being in gear with a flat toothed wheel at the top of the threaded spindle. As the work proceeded the spindle drew the chain tighter and pulled the bit through the steel being drilled.

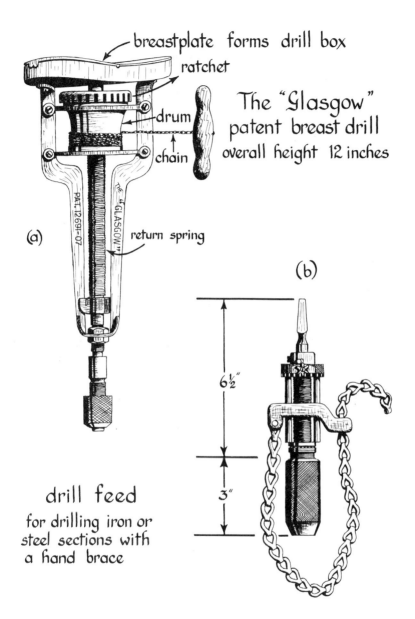

breastplate forms drill box

ratchet

drum

chain

The "Glasgow"
patent breast drill
overall height 12 inches

PAT.12691-07

THE "GLASGOW"

return spring

(a)

(b)

6½"

3"

drill feed

for drilling iron or
steel sections with
a hand brace

Figure 47   Drilling

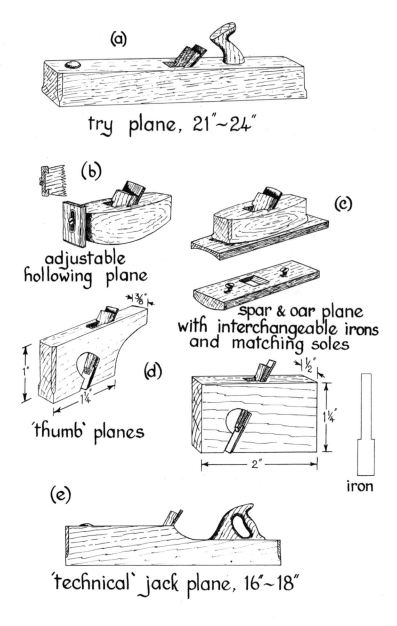

(a)

try plane, 21"~24"

(b)

adjustable
hollowing plane

(c)

spar & oar plane
with interchangeable irons
and matching soles

(d)

3/8"

1"

1¼"

'thumb' planes

½"

1¼"

2"

iron

(e)

'technical' jack plane, 16"~18"

Figure 48   Planes

Figure 48   Some of the planes usually found in the shipwright's tool chest, though most might have turned up in any woodworking or joinery shop.

Figure 48(a)   The standard wooden try plane, 21–24in long.

Figure 48(b)   This is perhaps peculiar to the ship- and boatbuilding trades, though some doubt has been cast upon its efficiency. I must confess that I have never tried out this example, which is in the Brixham Museum collection. It is a hollowing plane in which the curve which the sole would follow can be adjusted. This was done by raising or lowering a sliding block of wood on the fore end. Ranges of hollowing planes of fixed radius were also kept. They were used for a number of jobs on shipboard, but perhaps were best known for shaping out the 'spoon' or 'scallop' of oars.

Figure 48(c)   A spar and oar plane, and again I have chosen to illustrate an adjustable example. Fixed radius planes, for both inside and outside curves, were again commonly kept, but this version was also very often found. It has a complete set of interchangeable sole pieces, each marked with its radius, for both inside and outside curves, and to suit each sole there is an appropriate iron. These sets seem never to be found absolutely complete, as the parts tend to get separated. The most-used sole and iron are generally in the plane, but the irons that were used less often are usually lost.

Figure 48(d)   Two small home-made planes which, although common among cabinetmakers, are also found in the shipyard. These are 'thumb' planes, so-called because of their small size. Very simple wedge planes, they were made to suit small beadings, carvings and the cut for the gold stripe round a ship's hull. The variety was infinite. Blades were often cut and ground from old files, sawblades, pieces of scythe blade and so on.

Figure 48(e)   The 'technical' jack plane, a design very widely used in the nineteenth century. Just why 'technical' I have been unable to discover, the main differences appearing to be the letting down of the after half of the block, and the use of a closed handle instead of the open type.

Figure 49(a)   A tool that every shipwright seems to have owned was the plough plane. So many turn up of the home-made variety that I am forced to think that the apprentice shipwright was expected to make himself one. The plane I have illustrated has its parallels fastened to the guide block with copper nails riveted over a small square of copper in

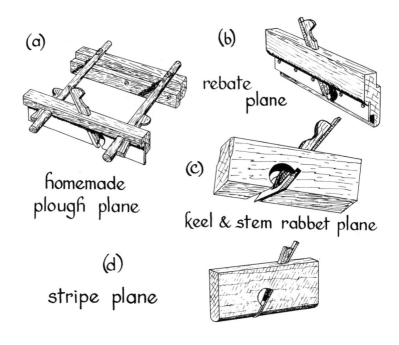

(a)

(b)

rebate
plane

homemade
plough plane

(c)

keel & stem rabbet plane

(d)

stripe plane

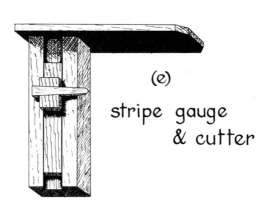

(e)

stripe gauge
& cutter

Figure 49   Planes, etc

the manner of a rove. The parallels are keyed to the plane with a pair of locked-in wedges. Many commercial ploughs are among those I have seen and found, some locked with wooden disc nuts, some with wedges, and one at least with brass thumb or wing screws.

Figure 49 (b)   A standard rebate plane, again a near standard part of the shipwright's outfit.

Figure 49(c)   A special version of the rebate plane, the keel and stem rabbet plane. This was wider than the usual rebate or rabbet plane, and the blade was set at a skew to the side to give a slicing action. It was used for cleaning out the rabbet cut from the head of the stem, and along the keel, to take the ends and edges of the planking. Its angle varied according to its position on the ship.

Figures 49(d) and (e)   These are better considered together. The stripe gauge (e) is not a very commonly found item, and its use may have been limited to a very few shipyards. It was run along the top of the bulwark rail the whole length of the ship to mark and partly cut the stripe, which, when finished, was usually filled with gold leaf. The blade was adjustable for the distance below the rail on a sliding piece which was clamped in by a wood screw from the other side. The stripe plane (d) is a simple round-bottomed plane which was used to clean up the stripe after either using the gauge and cutter or after gouging out the stripe. The size of stripe depended upon the size of vessel. Small ships of little more than 24ft sometimes had a stripe, but it was quite narrow. Here a thumb plane would be used for cleaning up.

Figure 50   A selection of types of wooden clamps used by boatbuilders when planking up clench-built boats. These went by the names of tongs, hutchits, grips or perhaps more commonly gripes. Their purpose and action is self-explanatory, as are their variations in design.

Figure 51(a)   This illustrates the enormous size of turnscrew--the original name for a screwdriver among all woodworking trades---used by shipwrights. Naturally such large tools almost invariably found themselves used as levers for some purpose or other, and many are found broken off above the widening of the blade. Even so, many were reground and used, some without even regrinding if the break was clean enough.

Figures 51(b) and (c)   These are more nearly normal sizes for turn-screws, and range from six to fifteen inches long. Apart from the greater length of the wooden handle on (a), these are really smaller versions of

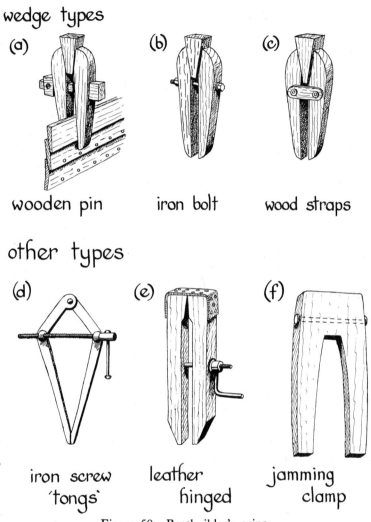

wedge types

(a)

(b)

(c)

wooden pin   iron bolt   wood straps

other types

(d)

(e)

(f)

iron screw   leather   jamming
'tongs'   hinged   clamp

Figure 50   Boatbuilder's gripes

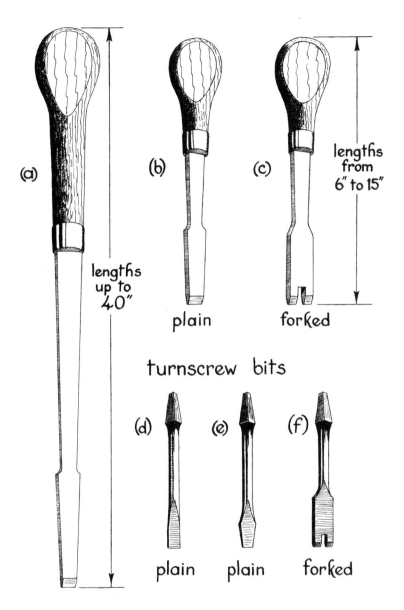

(a)

lengths
up to
40"

(b)

plain

(c)

forked

lengths
from
6" to 15"

turnscrew bits

(d)

plain

(e)

plain

(f)

forked

Figure 51   Turnscrews

the same thing. The forked type was used for saw screws, and nearly every user of a saw had his own turnscrews.

Figures 51(d), (e) and (f)   Turnscrew bits made to fit the ordinary brace. The first two forms are still commercially available.

Figure 52(a)   This could be described as a very heavy carpenter's sash cramp, but for its size. The size of the bar varied with the capacity of the cramp, as with the ordinary version. A cramp to take 4ft had a bar $4\frac{1}{4}$in by $\frac{3}{4}$in or 1in, and could weigh as much as 140 pounds. The great weight placed limitations on the size which could conveniently be used, and a 5ft cramp was about the largest used. They were used for straining in planking and cramping the framing of deck openings, among other jobs.

Figure 52(b)   The ceiling cramp, and perhaps this term ceiling needs explaining. The ceiling of a ship is the wooden lining fitted inside the frames of the vessel especially in the hold. It can cover the whole 'floor' and extends right up the sides to the deck beams. But it does not cover the lower side of the deck, as one might expect a ceiling to do. To fit this planking in place meant pulling it outwards to fit the inside curves of the hull. The ceiling cramp could be screwed into a hole in the frame and the sparring pulled in. This might be as much as three inches thick on some vessels.

Figure 52(c)   Another specialised cramp, used for pulling deck planking down to the beams. The ship has a curve from stem to stern at the deckline, sweeping upwards at the ends. This is known as the sheer. The deck planking, running fore and aft, has therefore to follow the inside of a curve. The decking cramp was used between the deck beams and carlings, with the leg slipped between them. The leg was slipped through a hole in a short timber which was retained by the key. This held the cramp down, so that the planks could be pulled downwards. A series of these cramps would be used along the length of the planking, working them across the ship between the beams, so that they did not call for too much dismantling.

Figure 52(d)   A typical example of the heavy sizes of G-cramp used in shipwork. These were used by the dozen in several sizes for cramping planks to the frames when planking up.

Figures 53(a), (b) and (c)   Various forms of bevel gauge found in shipwrights' tool boxes. The shipwright used gauges as much as any

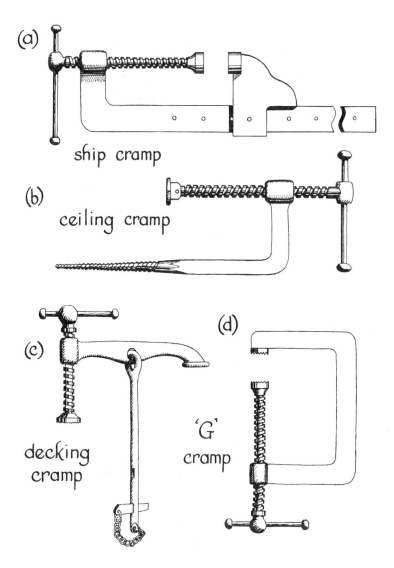

(a) ship cramp

(b) ceiling cramp

(c) decking cramp

(d) 'G' cramp

Figure 52   Cramps

(a) ebony or rosewood with brass

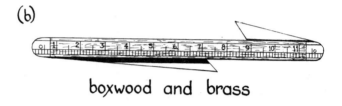

(b) boxwood and brass

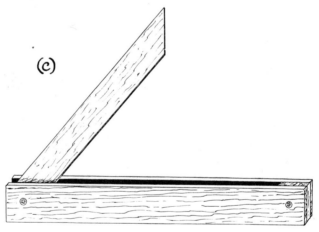

(c) homemade bevel, usually oak

Figure 53   Bevel gauges

other trade, but perhaps bevel gauges were used more than most. Their main use was in fitting the interior partitions and built-in furniture. The complex curves of a ship involve some very strange shapes and angles when it comes to fitting out. Some of these bevel gauges were quite elaborate, with ebony or rosewood boxes and brass bindings and leaves. Some, as in (b), were of boxwood with a scale engraved on them. Yet others were simple, home-made affairs of oak, with wooden pins and leaves, as in (c). From time to time other forms of gauge come out of the chippy's box, such as try squares, some of which are quite large, and spirit levels, which are surprisingly common. Their main task must surely have been in setting up keel blocks and sight lines.

Figures 54(a) and (b) The commonest forms of single-ended and double-ended nail pullers. The need for removing spikes and bolts for survey or repair existed in every shipyard. These were straight-forward levers with a 'trap' strap which helped to grasp the head of the nail.

Figure 54(c) An effective extractor known as a keel-bolt engine. This term 'engine' was used for almost anything which smacked of the mechanical, such as the screw pull of this tool.

Figures 54(d) and (e) Tools used to drive spikes down, known as spike setts. The earlier forms had withy handles, as did so many of the 'long-arm' variety.

Figure 55 A variety of scrapers used for cleaning down hulls, paintwork and the varnishing known as brightwork. Types (a), (b) and (c) are the oldest forms shown, though no doubt any shape would be made up if needed at any time.

Figure 56(a) A caulker's or caulking tool box of the type used in both Great Yarmouth and the Thames shipyards. The caulker sat on the carved wooden seat of the sliding lid when working, and the box, with its load of irons, was carried on the caulker's back by means of the haft of a caulking mallet pushed through the ring.

Figure 56(b) Another variation of the caulker's box, this time from Lowestoft, not so many miles distant from Great Yarmouth, yet the design is very different. The seat is padded, and access to the box is through a small round hole in the side. There is no lid. The hole also provides a handhold for carrying. One suspects that these boxes may well

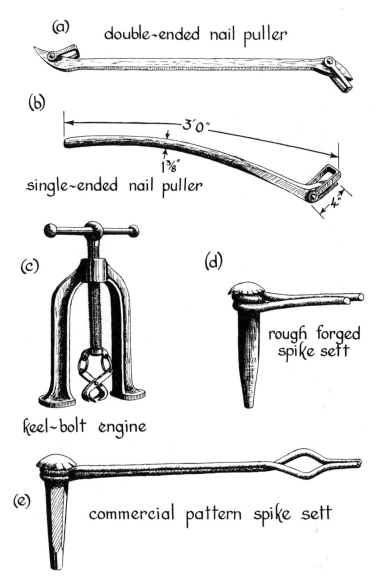

(a) double-ended nail puller

(b) 3'0"

1⅜"

4"

single-ended nail puller

(c) keel-bolt engine

(d) rough forged spike sett

(e) commercial pattern spike sett

Figure 54   Pullers and setts

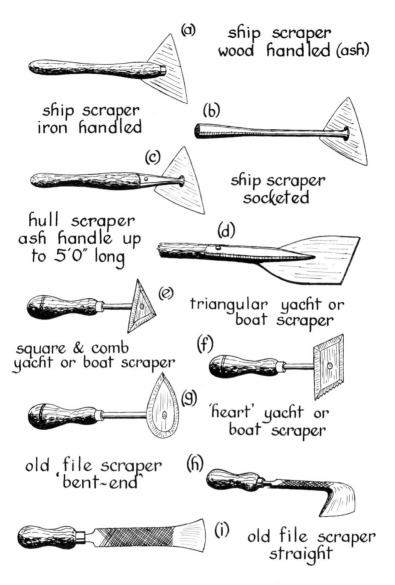

(a) ship scraper
wood handled (ash)

ship scraper
iron handled

(b)

(c) ship scraper
socketed

hull scraper
ash handle up
to 5'0" long

(d)

(e) triangular yacht or
boat scraper

square & comb
yacht or boat scraper

(f)

(g) 'heart' yacht or
boat scraper

old file scraper
'bent-end'

(h)

(i) old file scraper
straight

Figure 55   Scrapers

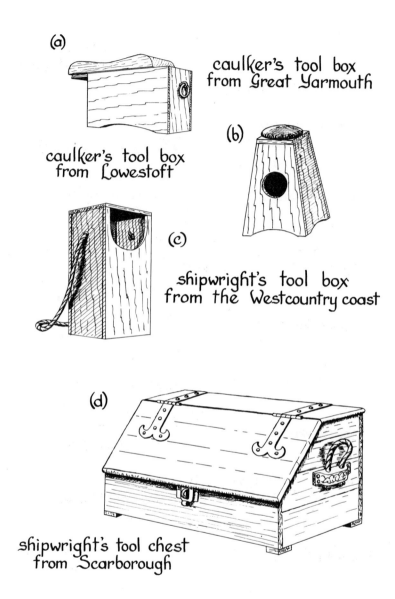

(a)

caulker's tool box
from Great Yarmouth

caulker's tool box
from Lowestoft

(b)

(c)

shipwright's tool box
from the Westcountry coast

(d)

shipwright's tool chest
from Scarborough

Figure 56　Tool. chests and boxes

have had a regional distribution, and it may be that the Lo'sterman's box is typical of the northern taste.

Figure 56(c)   A wooden tool box of the kind used in South West England. This is used as a caulking box, but it is also used more generally for shipwrightry. I suspect that its origin was in the caulking box, simply adapted as a convenient tool box for use on ships on the stocks. It is fitted with a rope strop, and I have seen boxes of this kind carried over the shoulder on adzes, mauls, caulking mallets and odd pieces of timber going down for fitting on the ship.

Figure 56(d)   An example of the tool chest used by the shipwright in the workshop. Some of these are most ornate pieces of work, others are quite plain. The slope of the top is deliberate, to prevent it being piled up under heaps of wood, tools and so on. The hinges on my example, which comes from Scarborough, Yorkshire, are rather ornate; others are much plainer, though the chippy seems to have preferred blacksmith-made hinges to the mass-produced types. The ends are fitted with rope strops fixed through wooden blocks, which are often elaborately carved. Sometimes the strops are intricately knotted with Turks' heads and other fancy ropework. These boxes were almost always painted, not varnished, generally in brown, red, black or green. Some were brighter, with white or yellow, but the more sober and hardwearing colours were more usually chosen. Inside the chests were fitted with a shelf and a few drawers up under the flat part of the top, and some had wooden cleats for saws fitted in the back.

Figure 57   A few of the more miscellaneous tools that were part of the ship- and boatbuilder's kit.

Figure 57(a)   An ordinary wad punch, which is a favourite tool of the boatbuilder to replace his roving iron.

Figures 57(b) and (c)   Two forms of roving irons. The roving iron was placed over the end of the copper nail when riveting a clench-built boat, to drive the rove home. The end of the nail was then cut or broken off and riveted down. Roves were generally round and slightly conical, but there were also square and diamond shapes, for which the special shape of roving iron was needed.

Figure 57(d)   A dolly which was used (at least on the North Devon coast, if not elsewhere) as a holder-up when riveting. Strapped round the knee, it was held against the head of the copper nail while the rove was being driven down.

155

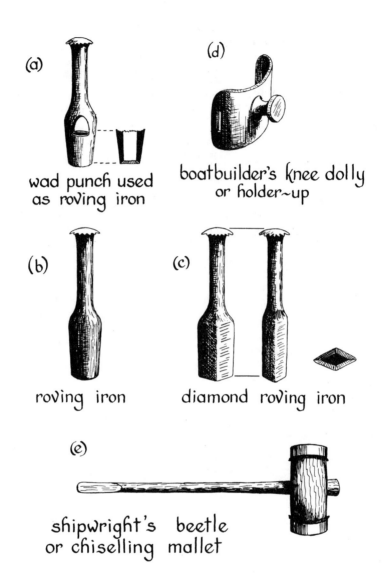

(a) wad punch used as roving iron

(d) boatbuilder's knee dolly or holder~up

(b) roving iron

(c) diamond roving iron

(e) shipwright's beetle or chiselling mallet

Figure 57   Miscellaneous tools

Figure 57(e)   The shipwright's beetle, bittle or chiselling mallet, a simple mallet with iron bands fitted on with oakum.

I have not illustrated the cutters used for clipping off the ends of copper nails, since the only survivors I have found have been rather modern end-cutters. Some earlier style must have been used, apart from the hammer with the breaking hole in the pein. These end-cutters are rather like sharpened pincers, but are hardly likely to have always been used. I have heard of nails being twisted off in the claw of a hammer, and this could have been a generally accepted method.

I have not been able to find a great deal of information about any particular working dress used by the shipwright. It is said that the ship-wrights of the North East coast, in the Shields area, wore a little square hat like that worn by the famous carpenter in Tenniel's drawings for *Alice in Wonderland*, but I am inclined to think that this may have been the ship carpenters, since the same hat is shown in nineteenth-century political cartoons to indicate the carpenters' unions. One specialised item was the jacket worn for caulking at Great Yarmouth, high-necked and buttoned down one side so that there was no danger of getting tools caught up. In spite of an intensive search, I have not yet found a photograph of these jackets in use.

I am quite sure that I have missed out many tools used by shipwrights and boatbuilders. It is almost impossible to achieve a complete list, since many tools were very local in use, and often made by the shipwright for one particular task. When one considers the complexity of shipbuilding and the variety of methods used to build ships, quite remarkable results were achieved. It is almost proverbial that the simpler a tool is, the better it functions, and perhaps this was the secret; after all, there is little we can do to improve the hammer.

5

THE SAILMAKER AND RIGGER

The sailmaker designed and made sails, canvas covers, dodgers, canvas cot bottoms (when ships carried these) and a variety of other items in varying grades of canvas and sailcloth. He also made one of the basic items of a sailmaker's gear, his own suit of clothing, which he made from light sail canvas. It was a two-piece suit, blouse and trousers, designed with no loose pieces to catch up threads or twine. The trousers had a flap front with side ties, and the blouse was drawn on over the head, with no buttons, just like a fisherman's blouse, which is designed not to catch in nets. The suits were partly to protect the wearer, and

John Janes' sail loft, Brixham

partly to protect his work. One might call them an early form of safety clothing. The sailmakers on p.158 are wearing these suits.

THE FIGURES

Figures 58(a), (b) and (c)   Two types of sailmaker's bench. This was the sailmaker's basic workplace, allowing long lengths of canvas to slide over his knees with support to the left. He could work along the length of the bench away from and against the pull of the stretching hook, which was fastened by stout twine to the right-hand end of the bench, avoiding the need to re-hook the canvas at too frequent intervals. The seat (the usual sitting position on the bench) was sometimes covered with a pad of canvas or a piece of carpet to make it a little more comfortable. By the sailmaker's right hand as he sat at his bench were several holes bored through the bench to take wooden or bone fids and a spool holder. The end of the bench here was enclosed by three pieces of wood to form a tray which prevented loose tools from rolling to the floor. Behind the seat a canvas bag hung down from the bench to hold small items such as grommets, brass eyelets, eyelet punches, cases of needles and so on. Tied to the front rail of the enclosed end was the stretching hook, or perhaps two. The lengths of benches varied tremendously, the usual being about seven or eight feet. All were of local manufacture, made to order by a local carpenter, so they do have a certain amount of individuality. The arrangement and number of fid holes varies, but the important point was that the fids, when housed, should not touch the floor.

Figure 59(a)   A wooden twine spool, rather like an oversize cotton reel, on which twine was wound and held on the pins of the spool holder. Seaming twine, of flax, was at one time purchased in skeins or hanks of raw or 'white' twine. For most sailmaking purposes this had to be tarred, then wound on the spools. Tarring was done in the loft using Stockholm tar. The barrel of tar was placed under a hook set in the loft wall, and the whole of the skein was dipped in the tar. It was then hung on the hook, and the sailmaker rubbed it down with his bare hands, rubbing the tar right into the twine until it would take no more. The skein would be almost dry when finished, and, to use a sailmaker's own words, 'yer 'ands reeked fer days'. The skein was then wound on to spools, using the spool winder. Modern twines are sold in cops, wound on spools made of compressed fibre.

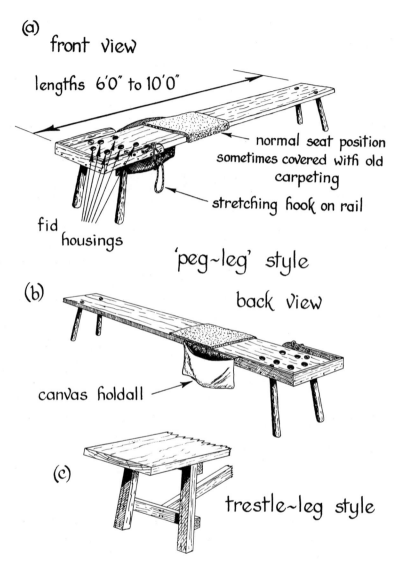

(a)

front view

lengths 6'0" to 10'0"

normal seat position
sometimes covered with old
carpeting

stretching hook on rail

fid housings

'peg~leg' style

(b)

back view

canvas holdall

(c)

trestle~leg style

Figure 58   The sailmaker's bench

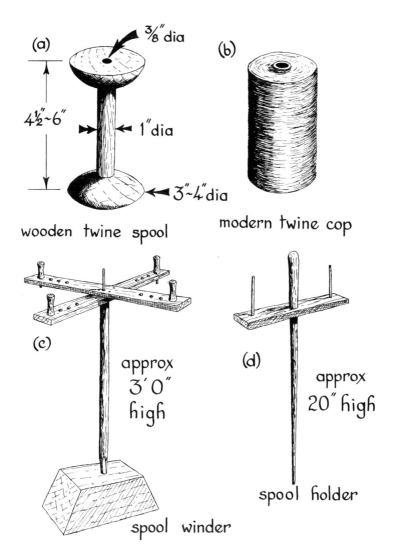

(a)

⅜" dia

4½"~6"

1" dia

3"~4" dia

wooden twine spool

(b)

modern twine cop

(c)

approx
3' 0"
high

spool winder

(d)

approx
20" high

spool holder

Figure 59

Figure 59(b) One of the modern twine cops, which the sailmaker can use in the same way on his spool holder, if he is still working in the old way.

Figure 59(c) A spool winder, which was used rather like a wool winder, the skein being placed round the pegs in the arms, and the spool loaded by hand, pulling the winder round. The spool winder had as its base a large block of wood on the loft floor. Other types are known, with a handle turning the spool and the arms set up at the end of a baseboard, rather like a large-scale version of the lacemaker's bobbin winder. The rather tiresome job of tarring and spool winding came to an end in the 1930s when the twine manufacturers started to produce cops of twine, either tarred, lightly tarred or white, wound on light spools. The earlier cops were wound on wooden spools. Smaller reels of the more familiar cotton-reel design were supplied for sailmakers' sewing machines, and today most of these are of plastic. The cops wound on cores instead of reels suffer from the disadvantage that loops of twine tend to drop off them when they are upright on the spool holder, and it became customary to tuck the loose end under the next loop and pull it fairly tight.

Figure 59(d) A typical spool holder, which stood in one of the holes in the end of the sailmaker's bench. The spools stood on the two pins.

Figures 60(a), (b), (c) and (d) Four varieties of what is really the same tool in slightly differing forms. The shapes seem to have dictated the names—sail pricker, pegging awl, and sail stabber. One of their basic uses was in laying out the design of a sail on a loft floor. Once designed, the sail was drawn out full size on the loft floor in chalk, with allowances for tabling, etc. (The tabling of a sail is what a dressmaker would call the hem, running right round the sail.) First the corners of the sail were drawn in and marked with sail prickers driven into the floor. In some lofts ordinary carpenter's bradawls were used for the same purpose, and many were needed. A length of twine was run round the prickers and drawn tight. The depths of roundings or hollows to be worked into the leach, luff and foot of the sail were measured off from the twine, and the line was defined as a curve either by using a long wooden spline bent round or a webbing tape 'thrown' along the line, held to a fair curve by more sail prickers, pegging awls or bradawls. The line was chalked in and the tabling widths drawn on. The bolts of canvas were then rolled across the pattern, taking into account the way the cloths were to run, and each piece was cut to size and pegged

162

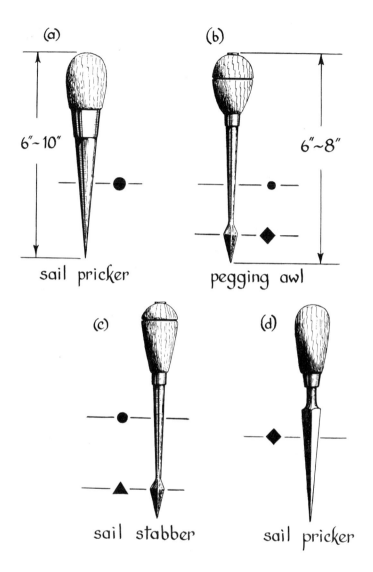

(a)

6″~10″

sail pricker

(b)

6″~8″

pegging awl

(c)

sail stabber

(d)

sail pricker

Figure 60

down with yet more awls or prickers, taking care that they did not cut any of the threads of the canvas. Allowance was made for the seams between the edges of the cloths, and for 'broad seams' by which the sail could be shaped to give any fullness or belly. A lot of prickers were used, and one suspects that the names may simply have been those given by various manufacturers. The sail pricker in (a) is a round tapered spike, not above ten inches long. When found larger than this it is a marline spike, the smaller sizes of which were often used on board ship for the same purpose. Figure 60 (b) is described as a pegging awl, which sounds more like the work it was to do, but the sail stabber in (c) only differs in being triangular in section instead of square. The sail pricker in (d) is really no more than a pegging awl with an elongated square tapered point. Although used for laying or pegging out, their other task was to open passages between the threads of canvas, without cutting them, to assist sewing.

Figure 61 The typical make-up of the corner of a sail, with the tablings, linings and corner patches. It was possible for there to be over a dozen thicknesses of canvas on a corner. If by some unfortunate circumstance the selected material happened to be No 1 canvas, this could be really heavy work. No 1 canvas is as stiff as thick millboard, and working it led to many broken needles, and stiff and very sore fingers.

Figure 62 The most commonly used seams worked by the sailmaker. These are purposely drawn 'loose' to show the details.
Figure 62(a) The flat seam used for joining two pieces of cloth edge to edge, and normally termed 'tabling'. The edges were lapped about 2in, and hooked into the sail hook. Both edges were then sewn, working away from the hook. Only one edge is shown being worked in my drawing. Tabling, the same term as that used to describe the 'hem' round the sail, was worked with the canvas flat across the knees, putting in about 144 to 180 stitches to the yard, or between 4 and 5 stitches to the inch, each stitch being at roughly 45°· to the seam.
Figure 62(b) The customary middle seam or 'sticking' which was added to the above to give it extra strength. It was also worked away from the hook, but in a straight line, using the same number of stitches as the tabling.
Figure 62(c) Another hand seam known as a round seam, used for

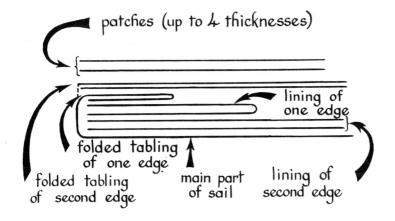

patches (up to 4 thicknesses)

lining of one edge

folded tabling of one edge

folded tabling of second edge

main part of sail

lining of second edge

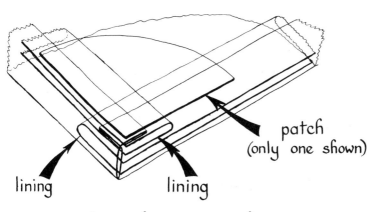

lining

lining

patch (only one shown)

typical make-up at the corner of a sail

Figure 61

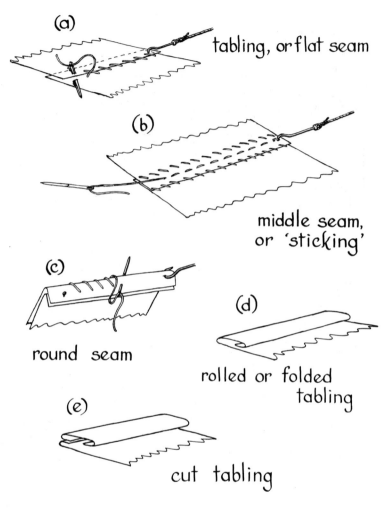

(a) tabling, or flat seam

(b) middle seam, or 'sticking'

(c) round seam

(d) rolled or folded tabling

(e) cut tabling

Figure 62   Various seams

joining two edges, particularly selvedges or selvages, and is considered to be the strongest of all hand stitching. One piece of material was hooked into the stretching or sail hook, taking care not to break any threads, and a fold about one inch wide was rubbed down with a seam rubber. It was then taken off the hook, the second piece placed inside, the whole hooked up again and the seam sewn towards the hook, holding the end against the hook.

The term 'putting together' was used to cover the sewing together of the various cloths which made up the sail.

Figure 62(d)   A rolled or folded tabling or hem used on some types of sail.

Figure 62(e)   A cut tabling used on the edges of sails.

Before sewing the tabling, it was first rubbed down with seam rubbers. The sail was placed on the floor on the drawn pattern and pegged out into place. The raw edges which were to form the tabling were turned over and rubbed down along the crease to give a fairly sharp edge. The tabling could be formed in one of two ways. If the edge was to be straight, and the crossed threads of the material did not give it a crossed bias, then a rolled or folded tabling could be used. But if the crossed bias was allowed it could cause nasty creases both when sewn and in use. In this case a cut tabling would be used. The tabling, leaving a small turning, was cut off and lifted bodily on to the sail without turning it over. The edges were turned under and the whole sewn together without any creases or cross bias.

Figures 63(a), (b), (c) and (d)   Typical seam rubbers used for producing sharp folds prior to sewing. They come in an endless variety of carved and fancy hardwood—never softwood which would wear and splinter. Even pieces of polished steel were used in many lofts, and special forms, as in (d), were produced to allow seams to be rubbed round roping in the edges. In modern lofts the tool is almost always steel, and known as a rubbing iron. The use of harder synthetic fibres is probably responsible for the change. The older sailmakers preferred wood, believing that the use of iron or steel might cause iron rot in the canvas; certainly for the sailmaker on board a ship at sea rust on an iron tool could be something of a nuisance.

Figures 64(a), (b) and (c)   Typical sail needles, with square or triangular points. There was a full range of sizes in all types. Most sail-

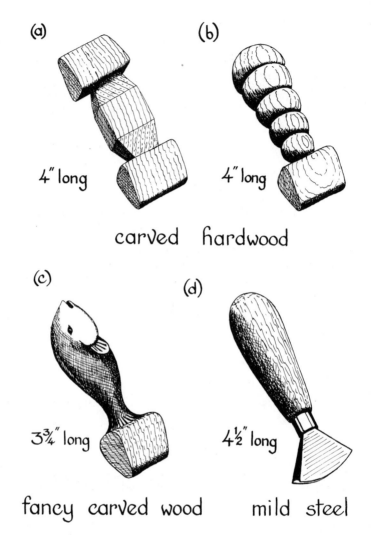

(a)

4" long

(b)

4" long

carved hardwood

(c)

3¾" long

(d)

4½" long

fancy carved wood   mild steel

Figure 63   Seam rubbers

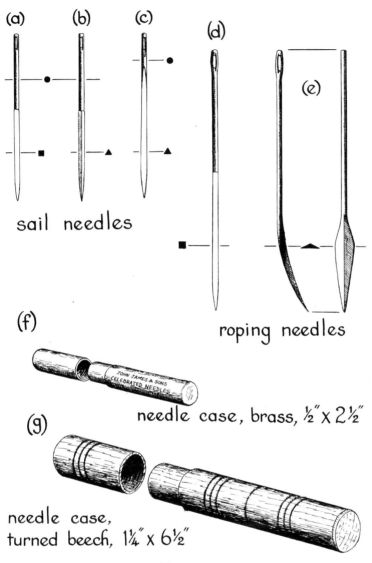

(a) (b) (c) (d) (e)

sail needles

roping needles

(f)

needle case, brass, ½″ x 2½″

(g)

needle case,
turned beech, 1¼″ x 6½″

Figure 64

makers had their own favourite designs, though they all followed the same general lines. The type shown in (c) had a longer triangular section than most, and Herman Thomas, the last survivor of the sailmakers who served their apprenticeships in a Brixham sail loft, told me that this was his own personal preference, since it carried the needle and thread almost right through the canvas before the threads closed.

Figures 64(d) and (e)   These are typical of the larger needles used for roping (sewing a rope to the edge of a sail). Hand roping is by no means easy work, and a good man is highly prized even by modern sailmakers. The big problem is to keep the work even. First the rope was laid out free of twists until it laid 'quietly'. Then a pencil line was drawn down the centre of the rope as a guide for sewing. The sail was laid out with the edge to be roped fair and even, and the rope laid down beside it. The correct amount of deduction from its length was calculated and the length cut. The rope was always shorter to allow for stretching. It was then stretched to the required length and marks struck at intervals. These intervals could vary according to how and where the stretch was needed. Similar marks, but at different intervals, were then made on the sail edge. The calculation of these intervals was part of the art of sailmaking, and I do not pretend to know it. The sewing commenced, matching mark to mark as the work went on, keeping the rope free of twist by the pencilled guide line. Machine roping gives a more even tension, though it is not so satisfactory in other ways, and the hand roper is still called in for heavy ropes or if the work is to be subject to much strain. Machine roping is not really strong enough to stand more than moderate strain, and in spite of the greater expense, hand sewing is still preferred.

Figures 64(f) and (g)   Two of the many styles of needle cases used by sailmakers. The small brass type were supplied at one time free of charge by the needle makers with the needles. The maker's name was stamped on the side. At the bottom of the tube was a small piece of oil-soaked wadding to prevent the points from rusting. The turned wooden case was very popular, especially for larger needles, and when carrying needles to and from a job away from the loft. These show such regularity in their design that I feel sure they were produced by the score on a commercial basis. They turn up in so many different places and are used for so many different things among the maritime communities that I am by no means convinced that they were solely made as sailmakers' needle cases. I have found them in marine engineering

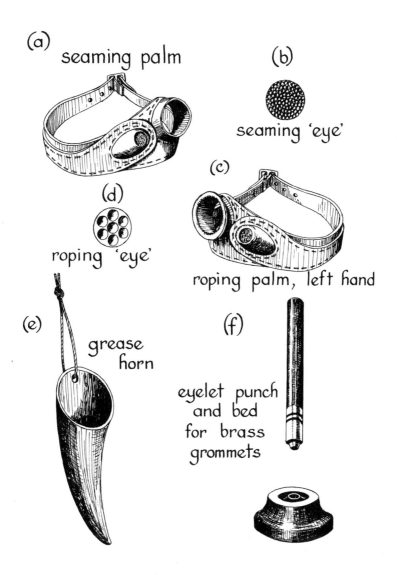

(a) seaming palm

(b) seaming 'eye'

(c) roping palm, left hand

(d) roping 'eye'

(e) grease horn

(f) eyelet punch and bed for brass grommets

Figure 65   Sailmaker's palms, etc

shops and elsewhere, holding small drills, fine files and other small tools. It is possible that they were supplied in bulk to small tool manufacturers generally.

Figures 65(a) and (b) The sailmaker's seaming palm and an enlarged sketch of the metal 'eye' which is fitted to it: This tool is the sailmaker's equivalent of the dressmaker's thimble, and the eye, a metal disc, has a series of close-set indentations to stop the needle slipping. This eye is set in a thick pad of leather which is, in turn, mounted on a leather strap. The eye sits on the heel of the palm of the sailmaker's hand, where it can support and protect the hand. At this point the whole weight of a man's forearm and arm muscles can be brought to bear to drive the needle through thick material. The thumb hole has a protective collar of leather round it. A turn of the sewing twine round this collar enables the sailmaker to pull his stitches tight without cutting his thumb.

Figures 65(c) and (d) A roping palm, which is similar to the seaming palm, except for the much heavier indentations in the eye and a thicker moulded leather guard to the thumb hole. These were necessary for the heavier needles and twine used when roping. This particular drawing is of a left-hand palm. The cast of the thumb hole is such that it is quite impossible to wear a right-handed palm on the left hand, and vice versa. To cope with the heavier work usually entailed, some roping palms are made of more solid and heavier leather than seaming palms.

Sewing palms of this kind were not exclusively the province of sail-makers. Most seamen at one time could, and were expected to be able to, use them. As a small boy in Surrey I remember well the first one I ever saw. It was kept in my grandfather's tool box. Grandfather was a gun-smith, and is said to have used the palm for making and repairing leather gun cases.

Figure 65(e) A grease horn, used by sailmakers to keep needles in. Strictly speaking, grease should read fat, for the horn was usually half full of lard. Grease causes rot in canvas, and was never used. The horn itself was either cow or sheep horn, usually sheep, fitted with a short lanyard. Keeping needles seems to have been a later use of the horn, its original purpose being to grease needles with lard before use. Some present-day sailmaking textbooks still say 'dip the needle in fat before sewing'. Some riggers also adopted the grease horn, in this case filled with grease for use on bottle screws. In this case a longer lanyard was used, and the horn was hung round the neck.

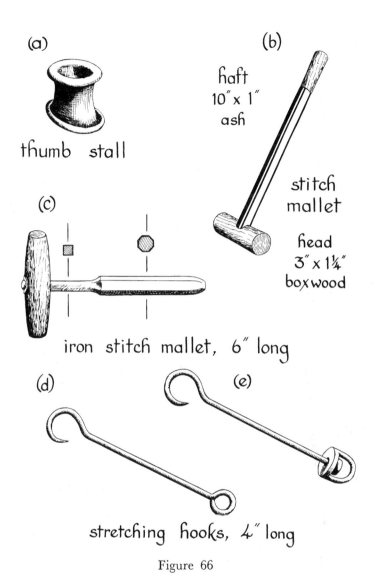

(a)

thumb stall

(b)

haft
10" x 1"
ash

stitch
mallet

head
3" x 1¼"
boxwood

(c)

iron stitch mallet, 6" long

(d)   (e)

stretching hooks, 4" long

Figure 66

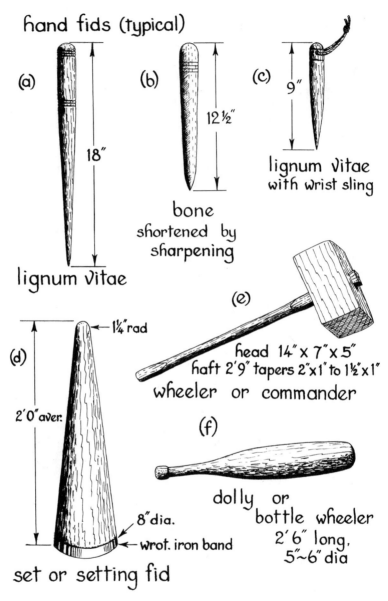

hand fids (typical)

(a)

18"

lignum vitae

(b)

12½"

bone
shortened by
sharpening

(c)

9"

lignum vitae
with wrist sling

(e)

head 14" x 7" x 5"
haft 2'9" tapers 2"x1" to 1½"x1"
wheeler or commander

(d)

1¼" rad

2'0" aver.

8" dia.

wrot. iron band

set or setting fid

(f)

dolly or
bottle wheeler
2'6" long,
5"~6" dia

Figure 67

Figure 65(f) A later tool of the sail loft which was introduced when brass spur-toothed grommets replaced many of the old rope grommets. It needs little explanation.

Figure 66(a) A thumb stall used for tightening stitches, which was used over the first half of the nineteenth century. It could be had either in moulded leather or brass, and was shaped to sit firmly on the slope of the hand at the base of the thumb.

Figures 66(b) and (c) Types of stitch mallet that again were for tightening stitches, used as levers rolling on the head of the mallet. That in (b) has a brass barrel fitted over the ash haft to take the wear of the twine. The iron version in (c) could be used either in the same way or with the twine wound round the octagonal part and the handle turned like a key.

Figures 66(d) and (e) The two commonest forms of stretching hooks, which spent their days tied to the end of the sailmaker's bench.

Figures 67(a), (b) and (c) Three typical examples of fids, which were wooden or bone spikes, used for opening holes in canvas, reaming out grommets, or splicing. They can be found in a variety of sizes and materials, the harder the material the better. Unfortunately they have become firm favourites with private collectors, with their high polish from years of use, and are now rather scarce. Rather than cut holes in the canvas of a sail, the sailmaker preferred to open up a gap between the threads. This might be started with a sail pricker or a kindred tool, then worked up with a wooden fid. To all intents and purposes the fid was a wood or bone version of the marline spike. It was important to preserve the point of a fid as long as possible, as a damaged end could ruin a sail, catching and tearing threads. Lignum vitae or bone were the usual materials. Sometimes they would be resharpened, but this reduced their value to some extent since the taper would be lost. Their housings in the end of the sailmaker's bench were designed to keep the points clear of the floor with this in mind.

Figure 67(d) The set or setting fid, a large wooden fid with a heavy iron band round its base so that it would stand steady on the loft floor when working cringles (see Figure 69, below). These came in a range of sizes, all about two feet or so long, but with different tapers. The one I show has a fairly blunt point and was used for large work. Others taper to a sharper point.

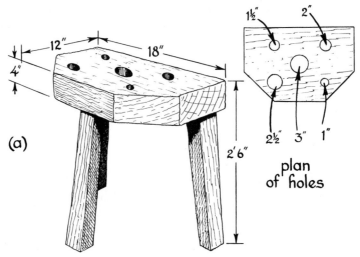

(a)

12"   18"

4"

2' 6"

1½"   2"

2½"   3"   1"

plan
of holes

fid stool or table
holes large enough to hold
fids near top of their taper

(b)

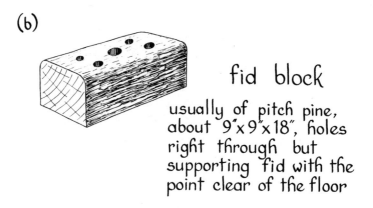

fid block

usually of pitch pine,
about 9" x 9" x 18", holes
right through but
supporting fid with the
point clear of the floor

Figure 68   Fid holders

Figures 67(e) and (f) Wheelers or commanders, the latter term being used when the tool was carried at sea. They were used for driving the rope cringles down over the set fid to expand them ready to sew into the sail. The type in (e) could also be used as a lever for tightening the roping twine. Two of these tools were used at a time, one working each side of the set fid. The example in (f) was found in a Padstow, Cornwall, sail loft associated with two set fids. The loft had been disused for many years, and the true purpose of the tool had been lost. I suspect it was used as a wheeler, and for want of a better name have designated it a dolly or bottle wheeler. It was found in 1968, the loft having been active in the 1920s, and it is known to have been in the loft at that time. Experienced sailmakers have told me that they consider it would have been better, in some ways, than the square wheeler particularly when beating down the sail to meet the grommet. The only other similar tools I know of are in the East Anglian Maritime Museum at Great Yarmouth, where they are thought to have been 'chokers' or hawse pipe stoppers. However, the high polish suggests a gentler use, associated with canvas and rope.

Figure 68(a) A simple fid stool or table, used to house the largest fids in the loft. The clearance above the floor was needed to keep the points off the floor.
Figure 68(b) An even simpler method of housing fids, though in this case the short ones. A block of pitchpine with holes bored through it, it could be moved about the loft for use wherever the sailmaker might be.

Figure 69 The method of working a cringle into a sail, using the set fid. Grommets and cringles were made from rope. In the case of a cringle which might be used for the main reef points, a length of suitable rope about eight feet long was cut, then untwisted into its three component strands. By winding each strand up into its original twist, three cringles, each with two ends, could be formed. Rope grommets were made up similarly, but the tails were left one-third and two-thirds in length, then plaited together to give a single flat tail, tapered by reducing the thickness of the strands progressively. Special patches were sewn in the sail to take the grommets, with up to four thicknesses of canvas. In Figure 69(a) the grommets are shown sewn down to their patches on the inside of the roped sail edge. The tails are sewn down firmly on the patches. The cringle itself was worked through the two grommets and

177

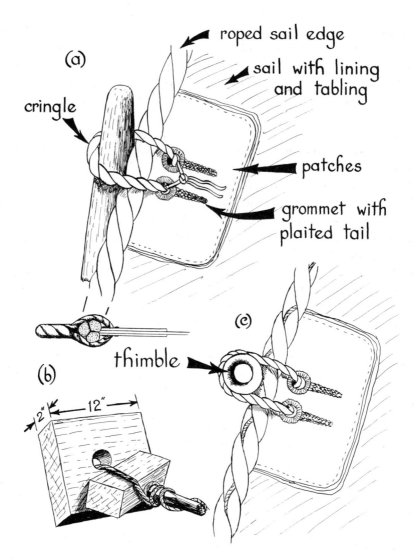

(a)

roped sail edge

sail with lining
and tabling

cringle

patches

grommet with
plaited tail

(b)

thimble

(c)

12″

2″

Figure 69   Working a cringle

over the roped edge to form a single loop, by putting the strand through one grommet with about one-third on one side, and two-thirds on the other, then twisting it back on itself and through the other grommet to make up a three-strand loop. The two ends were drawn through the grommets and tied together. The cringle was then placed on the top of the set fid and driven down hard with the wheelers. When sufficiently stretched the cringle was slipped off the fid and a galvanised steel thimble driven in as quickly as possible before the rope shrank back to its original size. The tied ends were loosed and strained tight. A common way of doing this was to use a 12in square of 2in-thick wood, as in Figure 69(b), with a hole in the centre. The tails were passed through this hole and strained up, one at a time, using the wheeler, as shown. The ends were then led up to the bolt rope on the sail and spliced in. The extreme ends of the tails were divided and tied firmly round one of the strands of the boltrope. The completed cringle appeared as in Figure 69(c).

An older method of fitting cringles was to fid out two holes between the canvas and the boltrope, and form the cringle through this and the strands of the boltrope itself. This tended to weaken the boltrope at a rather vital point, and the grommet method was far superior. The holes for grommets were at one time cut out with a knife, but later practice used a circular wad punch on a block of wood. The holes were always punched on the end grain of the wood. If the side was used the hole would never punch out clean.

Cutting out seems always to have been done with a knife, not, as might be expected, with shears or scissors. There does not seem to have been any regular form of cutting knife, but knives tend to be used to destruction or carried away for other purposes when their working life in the loft is done. The experience of Herman Thomas, throughout his sailmaking career, was that a table knife, broken off about three inches from the handle and ground with a sloping point, was ideal. 'Not a stainless steel one, of course,' he told me. The old idea that stainless steel will not hold a sharp edge is a deeply ingrained one. I personally suspect that this is because it requires less cleaning. The cleaning of a dirty knife blade plays an important part in the maintaining of a sharp edge.

The making of good sails was indeed an art; only by long experience could these men know exactly how much to allow in a sail of a certain material, roped with a certain size and type of rope, for it to set perfectly and stretch evenly. An example of how they relied upon the known

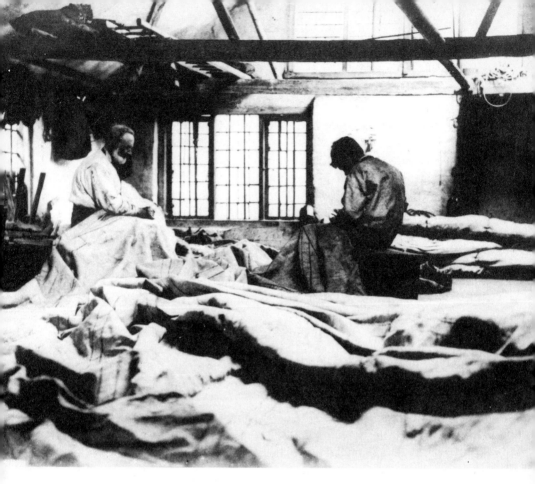

A Yarmouth sail loft, about 1885

characteristics of their materials was vividly brought to light some years ago when a large rope manufacturer made a very slight alteration to the treatment he gave to his rope in the finishing. It was a very minor thing, yet from all over Britain came reports of sails not setting as they should. On investigation the sailmakers discovered the new treatment being given to the ropes, which was of such a minor nature that the ropemaker had not even bothered to notify them. Yet it made sufficient difference in the stretch of the rope over the size of the sail to affect their set considerably. By altering the allowances the fault was corrected.

The stretching of sails when only natural fibre cloths were used was most important. Many sailmakers insisted on being the first to hoist the new sails, and gave strict instructions on how the sails were to be run in. Otherwise they might not accept any responsibility whatever, and were even known to refuse to supply the sails, made up though they might be. In Weston Martyr's book, *Southseaman*, there is a passage describing how the Nova Scotian sailmaker handled the new sails, and how all hands were rushed to his garden to help take the sails in when it started to rain, for fear they would distort. The sailmaker was truly one of the old school, with his own secret methods of 'curing' the canvas after making up, which included, apparently, hanging them out in the garden. But a collection of rainwater in the cloth could distort the sail, to say nothing of patches shrinking from simply getting wet. These old sailmakers were loath to part with their secrets, other than to their own apprentices when the time came. As fewer apprentices took up the trade, so the secrets died with their owners.

The old sailmaker had no tables of stresses and strengths, elasticity and so on worked out from carefully designed tests to guide him. He worked entirely from the great collection of experience passed on to him and often learned the hard way. The laying down of certain specifications by the British Admiralty probably brought about the first standardisation of the products of the sailcloth mills. Before this, and for many years after, each manufacturer's materials were different from the next. The sailmaker needed to apply his own private tests to each new batch of material delivered to him.

At some time during the last quarter of the nineteenth century sewing machines were introduced into the sail loft, at first being of the treadle type, leaving both hands free to control the canvas. A few hand machines were also used, but I gather that they were not very popular. Modern machines are a far cry from the old types. Today they have double needles and a pull feed instead of the old claw, to give an even tension (like the old sail hook), and the weight of the sewn cloth is carried on travelling tables. These are a great improvement, as the weight of a sewn sail can be very difficult to manage when the last few stitches are being put in. The pull feed, too, is a great improvement on the older claw feed, which is still used on the smaller domestic sewing machines. Claw feed worked only on the lower piece of the two cloths being put through, with the result that there could be different tensions in the pieces being joined. Heavy cloths are sometimes too heavy for the double-needle machines to take, and may have to be worked by passing twice through a heavy single-needle machine, or even by hand. In fact, hand sewing, although it takes much longer, is still far superior on the natural fibre materials. It is stronger, and can be pulled tighter. With flax or cotton canvases the hand sailmaker can bed the twine right into the sail material, which the machine does not. In the case of terylene sails this is not the case, and the threads lie on the surface whichever method of sewing is used. But handsewn terylene work is done with a heavier waxed twine than that used on the machine, and will last much longer.

Mention has already been made of the use of a machine in roping sails, but there are limits on the size of boltrope which can be handled in this way, and drawbacks over the tension. This may not be so important with boltropes of man-made fibre, but the thickness that can be sewn is still limited. With these newer materials the tendency is for the old boltrope to give way to tapes of synthetic fibre. As the techniques and materials improve, this can be expected to spread to larger sail sizes, and the machine will come into its own in this field.

THE RIGGER

The rigger worked very closely with the sailmaker, often sharing a loft and even maintaining a common stock of materials. They would help each other with rigging and fitting the yards, and in bending the sails and equipping them with the relevant sheets and so on. The only tools I have been able to find, other than those already covered in this book, are illustrated in the following figures.

THE FIGURES

Figures 70(a), (b) and (c)   Three examples of spikes used by riggers for splicing, dating from the end of the eighteenth century. The rigger had available all the range of wooden fids used by the sailmaker, and even used the sharper types of set fid for some very heavy splicing, but the iron spikes seem to have been his own province. The marline spike here has a turned end, but in other respects is very similar to the iron fid, which I have not come across elsewhere described as a fid. The second marline spike, (b), is a smoother iron or steel tool, again with the turned end, but this time with a button top.

Figures 70(d) and (e)   Wooden serving boards of the same period, but as they are taken from illustrations it is difficult to see how they were used. It is quite clear that they could be used, and they may have had a groove on the underside to take the rope. Serving boards and serving

182

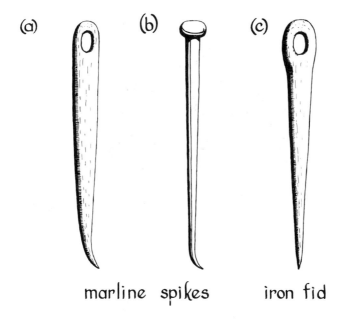

marline spikes   iron fid

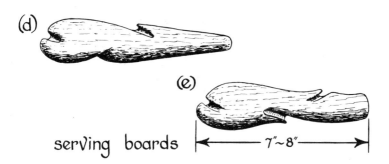

serving boards

Figure 70   18th-century riggers' tools

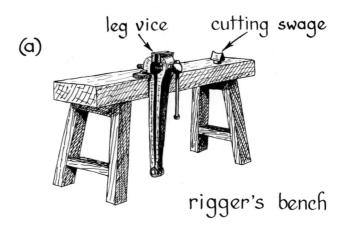

(a)

leg vice cutting swage

rigger's bench

(b)

rigger's screw

Figure 71   Riggers' tools

mallets were both used for applying a twine wrapping or serving to protect a splice in rope, see p.187.

Figure 71(a)   The only kind of workbench I can find associated with the rigger, and I strongly suspect that it only came into use after the adoption of wire rope for rigging. The top is frequently quite narrow— some being little more than a 6in-square baulk on four legs—and they are not often more than four feet long. The leg vice is not a special one, but usually adapted from an engineer's vice without the leg being fastened down to the floor. Sometimes a straightforward plain vice was used bolted to the top, but the leg vice gave a wider jaw for gripping wire ropes and loose strands. Towards one end of the bench was a blacksmith's cold cutting swage set roughly in line with the vice for cutting off surplus wire.

Figure 71(b)   The standard form of rigger's screw—not to be confused with a rigging screw, which is one type of bottle screw used in setting up a ship's rigging—which was employed in wire splicing to pull the strands together and harden down. There are several sizes, some being up to four feet long, others little more than a foot. All have the open end retained by a key, with at least two positions for the key.

Figures 72(a), (b) and (c)   Types of modern marline spikes, used especially today in splicing wire. That in (a) is a wooden-handled one which might easily be confused with a sailmaker's sail pricker except that it runs to larger sizes. Those in (b) and (c) are no more than rather cleaner versions of the eighteenth-century tools, except that the end is no longer turned. In this they more readily relate to the iron fid than the earlier marline spikes. Today they are used for opening out the wire strands for splicing, whereas in earlier times they would have been used for fibre ropes. In this the turned end may have been an advantage.

Figure 72(d)   This is a more modern instrument introduced to help in wire splicing, dating from the late nineteenth or early twentieth century. The splicing iron was worked through the strands until the groove lay under the chosen strand. Then the wire being spliced in was slid along the groove. In spite of its obvious advantages, it does not seem to have been used a great deal, and is not so commonly found as might be expected. It is possible that it has sometimes been confused with a screwdriver when it has turned up among riggers' tools, which could account for its apparent scarcity in the records.

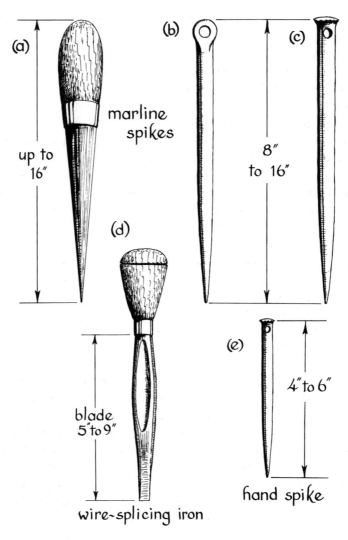

(a)

marline
spikes

up to
16″

(b)

(c)

8″
to 16″

(d)

(e)

blade
5″to9″

4″to6″

hand spike

wire-splicing iron

Figure 72   Splicing spikes

Figure 72(e) A small version of the iron marline spike which went by the name of hand spike. As with the straight marline spikes and some of the fids, it had a hole for a wrist strop, but it is not over 6in long. The marline spike was normally from 8in up to 16in or longer. Often enough the hand spike was used more for tightening and loosening screw shackles than anything else, though I know of it having been used to splice some very light wires.

Figures 73 (a) and (b) These show the method used to worm, parcel and serve a piece of rope. This might be done over a splice or in some part which was liable to exceptional chafing. Worming consisted of filling up the spaces between the strands of a rope with a light line, such as spun-yarn, to bring the surface more or less level for parcelling. Some small ropes and some of the larger wire ropes present a nearly level surface without a spiral 'groove' between the strands, and in these cases the worming could be left out. The worming might be laid in as tightly as possible by hand, or it might be strained in and hauled tight into the lay of the rope with a serving mallet or board, with a piece of rather heavier but softer rope known as a 'soft strand' to drive it in. Figure 73(a) illustrates this, with the serving mallet being used as a Spanish windlass. Parcelling was a wrapping of strips of tarred canvas, about two to three inches wide, wrapped on in the direction of, or 'with', the lay of the rope. Each turn overlapped the last one by about half an inch to give a continuous cover. Over the parcelling came the serving or whipping. The term 'serving' is used when this is put on to protect a splice, but when used to prevent the end of a rope from unlaying it is referred to as whipping. The serving was usually of spunyarn, hauled down with a serving mallet or board. It was put on against the lay of the rope, so that the parcelling and serving crossed each other. One of those little rhymes so popular among seafarers, and so invaluable to the illiterate, tells how the process should be done.

> Worm and parcel with the lay,
> Turn round and serve the other way.

Even with this simple rhyme there are variations of wording, but they all boil down to the same thing.

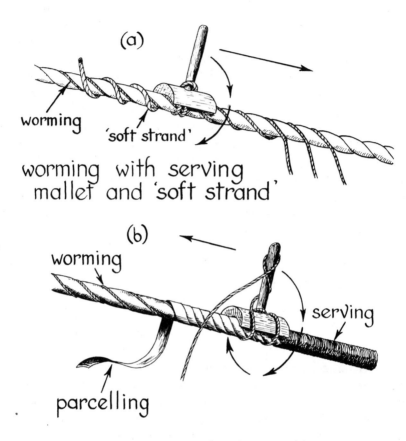

(a)

worming

'soft strand'

worming with serving
mallet and 'soft strand'

(b)

worming

serving

parcelling

serving with the mallet

Figure 73   Worming, parcelling and serving

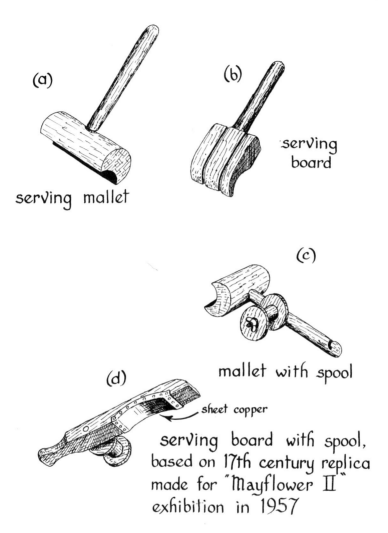

(a)

(b)

serving board

serving mallet

(c)

mallet with spool

(d)

sheet copper

serving board with spool, based on 17th century replica made for "Mayflower II" exhibition in 1957

Figure 74   Serving boards

Figure 74(a)   This shows the usual form of serving mallet which was used for applying the serving. It looks like a round-headed mallet with a groove along the length of the head. The grooves worn by the spunyarn when serving are always very distinctive, and indeed they could be so deep as to render the tool unusable except on light ropes. As Figure 73 shows, it worked round the rope, the handle acting as a lever.

Figure 74(b)   A simple variant of the mallet, the serving board. This is an older tool than the mallet, which seems to have come in during the early part of the nineteenth century to replace the board. In action it is exactly the same, but it bears on the top of the rope, using it as a fulcrum for its own leverage.

Figure 74(c)   This shows yet another variant, this time being a serving mallet with a spool for the spunyarn. Normally a second hand was needed to pass the spunyarn round the rope being served in front of the mallet, but the spooled mallet solved this problem and also prevented tangling.

Figure 74(d)   I have included for what it is worth. It is a so-called 'replica' of a spooled serving board which was made for the exhibition held at Brixham in connection with the construction of *Mayflower II*. Just where the information for this came from I have no idea, but quite frankly I cannot see how it was expected to work. To be effective the cord or spunyarn must run over the end of the board, otherwise the board cannot operate. It must also have a bar to work round, as provided by the haft of the mallets or board already shown. In this replica, now in the possession of Brixham Museum, this is not possible. I have even tried it, but it just does not work. Perhaps I have worked along preconceived lines, and not seen the obvious, but I suspect that any serving which might be applied by this tool would need replacing every time the rope was used, if it could be applied at all.

There are a few other tools I should mention which might be found in a modern rigger's loft, one being a machine used for a mechanical method—a proprietary one—of splicing smaller wire ropes of the kind often used on small yacht rigging, and a kind of winch which works by ratchet to haul wire ropes taut. There are two varieties of these, one being a heavy model which is bolted down to the loft floor, with a segment of a gear wheel on which the ratchet works, the other a portable machine which is mounted on the standing part of the wire and pulls the other strand—secured round a post—by a lever working on a ratchet principle. The same type of machine is used in coal mines as a pit prop

190

puller, and in a number of other jobs. The shackle pin maul, which has already been mentioned in the section on shipwright's tools, filled most of the hammer requirements of the rigger. A bolt cropper can also be found in modern lofts; it replaces the old cutting swage on the bench, and is a good deal more portable.

Wire splicing was considered the worst task of the rigger's trade by many of the men who did it. Wires vary not only in their construction, but in their individual flexibility, and it was only too common for riggers working on wire after a spell on fibre ropes to go home with torn and bleeding hands at the end of the day, only to turn up next morning to start again in bandages. By the end of the second day the bandages themselves had often been pierced and were soaked in blood.

191

6

THE ROPEMAKER

Ropemaking is one of those ancient crafts which must have been carried out in some way or other since the first natural fibres were twisted together to make some kind of cord. We know the Egyptians made ropes, not only from their illustrations but from samples of their actual products. The oldest known piece of rope, in the museum at Cairo, was found in the tomb of Hemaka at Saqqara, in almost perfect condition, and approximately 5,300 years old. In May 1942, another find was made in Egypt. This consisted of seven very thick papyrus ropes in the Tura Caves. It was reported that one was attached to a block of stone calculated to weigh sixty-eight tons, assumed to have been destined for the pyramids. Among the materials known to have been used for ropemaking by the Egyptians were papyrus, flax, rawhide (or leather) and palm fibre. It is possible that cotton was also used, but I have a suspicion that the famous Egyptian cotton was introduced from elsewhere at a much later date.

In England, ropemaking was a thriving industry in the days of King Alfred, and he himself spoke highly of the ropeworkers in the ninth century. Although ropemaking was widespread, and even the Admiralty had its own ropewalks incorporated in the Royal Dockyards, the production of marine ropes seems to have been concentrated at an early date in those areas where the best hemp could be grown. In England these areas were around Bridport in Dorset, and in parts of Somerset, where the conditions seem to have been about right. The rich damp soils of these areas produced fine hemp, or, to give it some of its older names, gallows grass or neckweed, an allusion to its use by the hangman. The industry at Bridport thrived for centuries, and is still represented there today by the netmaking industry, which is its direct descendant. King John is said to have had a hand in the establishment of the industry at Bridport in the thirteenth century. Whatever the truth of

A roper at work, Great Yarmouth, 1885

this, there was certainly a high concentration there at an early date. The walks can hardly have been very large ones, since at one stage St Michael's Lane, Bridport, is said to have had as many as forty walks in it.

Ropemaking in England underwent a drastic change about the year 1500, when the tackle board was invented. This was a device with several hooks on it, all turning at the same constant speed, which allowed the spinning of several yarns all of the same tension. Before this a single hook, spinning one yarn at a time, was used. From 1500 onwards English ropes were considered the finest available, with evenly spun yarns giving greater strength and evenness to the finished rope.

The coastal ropewalks seem to have been the first to feel the crunch when machine-made ropes came in during the nineteenth century, and few survived for long after 1900. Ropemaking is one of the crafts which has benefited from mechanisation, in that the machine-made rope is far superior to the handmade article. Its even winding and tension give it a more reliable strength and its statistical stretching and breaking strains soon established more confidence in it than in the older types. For marine purposes it was ideal, and it was soon taken up. A few coastal walks survived in areas which had a specific requirement, such as the supply of trawl warps for the fishing industry at Brixham, but these were few and far between. Inland walks survived longer, some still producing small quantities of string or twine, but very little of the old wooden machinery seems to have escaped the ravages of time and the wood beetle once it ceased to be in regular use. From what little I have seen of the inland and rural roperies, their equipment was not so elaborate or sophisticated as that employed by the ropers making marine ropes, and it may therefore not be fair to use them as a basis for this chapter. As far as possible, therefore, I have drawn on maritime or coastal sources.

The place where ropes were made was commonly called a ropewalk by the nineteenth century, though this was not always the case. Until the middle of the seventeenth century, or thereabouts, the term more often used was ropeground, since it was most commonly in the open without any cover. If it had a roof it was a ropehouse, and this term hung on in the Royal Dockyards, where the ropehouses produced most of the rope used by the Navy. The larger ropewalks were divided length-wise down the centre; on one side hemp was continuously spun up into yarns, and on the other yarns were first spun into strands and then the strands were laid up into rope. The two sets of gear were permanently set up, sometimes with a track for the drags or sledges and topcarts. Smaller walks often used a single undivided area, though with the gear still permanently set up at what was known as the head or fore end. The other end of the walk was known as the foot. The distance between the two could be anything up to half a mile, though most of the coastal walks were shorter, 800 to 1,000 feet being common. Provided that it was straight, the walk might take any form, open, covered, partly covered or lined on one or both sides with walls, sheds, buildings or just trees to give a little protection from the elements. Usually one side at least was open throughout the length. Some of the old ropehouses in the Royal Dockyards were covered entirely, only being open at the two ends. Whether the walks were covered or not, the ropers worked up and down the length of them day after day, rain or shine. They were a tough race of men, and the work was dirty and arduous.

In the early years of the present century Charles Gregory, a Brixham man, compiled a guide book to his home town entitled *Brixham in Devonia*. His biographical notes tell us that he was born in 1846, one of nine children of poor parents, his father being a fisherman. Gregory stayed at school until 1855, leaving when a rigger named Roberts called at the school looking for a boy to help him rig a schooner. Charles Gregory, aged nine, got the job at 1/6 (7½p) per week. The job was finished in a fortnight, and the lad was paid off, but he did not go back to school. He found another job, in one of the ropewalks, and for the same wage. He worked from 6am to 6pm for six days a week, only Sunday being free. The job entailed turning the wheel for spinning yarns and laying ropes for about eleven hours each day. Gregory stuck this until he was twelve years old, when he was bound apprentice to a smack owner to learn the trade of trawler. Trawler was the correct usage at that time, not trawlerman.

Compare this with the information I was able to obtain on a tape-recording at Brixham Museum in 1958. The following is a verbatim transcript, the initials standing for the speakers:

CA—the late Charles Ashford
JSC—J. Stanley Churchill
WSD—the late William Smerdon Dart
JEH—the author

The tape transcript is unedited, and I have done my best to convey the broad Devon accent without making the whole thing unintelligible.

CA : I worked in a ropewalk when I was thirteen years of age.
JEH : Would you tell us about that, Mr Ashford?
CA : We 'ad to start at six o'clock in the morning.
JSC : Was it Mr Elliott's?
CA : Mr Varwell's, up 'ere, Furzeham. Start six o'clock in the morning, winter and summer—and we 'ad to spin, I think it was, ten threads before breakfast, nineteen after breakfast, and thirteen in the afternoon—that was a day's work. The men 'ad to spin those amount of threads.
JSC : All done by manpower—
CA : We 'ad to 'eave the wheel then for these men to spin the threads, but then for to make the warps there was thirteen strands [threads] in every lissom, and four lissoms in every warp, and then it was all pulled out by horsepower. Pulled out down through the ropewalk, and after 'e 'ad the number of lissoms, that's like we call the strands, you see, they 'ad to lay them up, make the strands into one big thing, of four strands, well that was done, was done by manpower.
WSD : And they were—'ow many fathoms?
CA : There's—160 fathoms, two fifties and a sixty.
WSD : They could only make fifty fathom, at Furzeham?
CA : Oh, no, we could make longer, but that's the length the trawlers wanted, two fifties and a sixty, made 160 fathom long.
JSC : Splice 'em together.
CA : And splice 'em together, yes—and those warps used to cost somewhat about thirty pounds a set, twenty-eight to thirty pounds a set. These warps, by the way, would last a trawler—on the average—twelve months.
WSD : And then they'd be used for roundings.
CA : For making footropes like this [indicating part of a model trawl net], yes.
WSD : For making that rounding round the footrope.
JEH : How many days of the week did you work like that?
CA : Er—'ad to work Saturday's up to one o'clock.
JEH : Half a day Saturdays.
CA : That's right, half a day Saturday.
JEH : How much a week did you get for that?
CA : I 'ad—as a boy—I 'ad 2/9d [13.75p] a week. I 'ad 2/9d a week as a boy, and if I lost a quarter I should lose three'a'pence.

When Charles Ashford started in the ropery it was only being kept going by the demand for trawl warps, heavy hawser-laid ropes about ten inches in circumference (ropes are always measured by the circum-

196

The late Charles M. Ashford at work in his forge, Brixham, about 1925

ference), almost all the lighter ropes being more cheaply and efficiently produced by machinery elsewhere. Charles Ashford was working in the ropewalk about 1902, nearly fifty years after Charles Gregory, but doing the same job. He also left to take up an apprenticeship, being bound at the age of fourteen to a blacksmith, eventually becoming his own master. His photograph, taken in his own smithy in about 1925, is shown on p.197.

Comparing the two experiences shows up a number of improvements in conditions. Charles Gregory started work when he was nine, Charles Ashford at thirteen. Gregory was apprenticed at the age of twelve for nine years, Ashford at fourteen for seven years. Gregory's pay at age nine and Ashford's at thirteen can show little, if any change, although Ashford worked five hours a week less (Saturday afternoons), but for the rest of the week the hours were still 6am to 6pm. Breaks were unchanged, fifteen minutes each for breakfast and tea, thirty minutes for lunch. Ashford made no mention of ill-treatment, but Gregory, when he started his apprenticeship, suffered at the hands of a brutal skipper, too fond of wielding a rope's end. After one such spell of ill-treatment, he ran away from his ship, but returned the same morning. Nevertheless, in accordance with the letter of his indentures, he was dragged before the local magistrate and had to serve fourteen days in Exeter prison as a thirteen-year-old boy. He did not return to trawling after this.

The brutality of some of the trawler skippers (particularly those working out of Hull, where a boy was murdered and his body thrown overboard) brought about the introduction of the Merchant Shipping Act of 1886, which placed the responsibility for the welfare of seafaring apprentices in the hands of the marine superintendent at the local custom house. At the same time the terms of apprenticeships were reduced. Forster's Elementary Education Act of 1870 seems to have had the effect of reducing the term from nine years to seven; the 1886 Act reduced it still further to five years. The Coal Mines Act of 1842, which regulated the employment of children in the coal mines and some other industries, had no effect on seamen of any kind, though the abuses were just as bad.

A few years after Charles Ashford left the ropewalk in Brixham, the two surviving walks closed down. This was about 1910, and from then on trawl warps were purchased from mechanised ropewalks elsewhere.

Hemp, the basic material for English ropemaking, was harvested twice a year, once in July and again in September. The male plant

A Great Yarmouth ropewalk, 1885

matures in July, the female in September, and this latter needs threshing to remove the seed heads. The English crop had a staple of between three and four feet. When cut the hemp was tied into bundles of roughly a yard in diameter, left to dry for twenty-four hours, then threshed to remove the seed with the traditional wooden flail. The stalks were then reduced to fibre by fermentation, and this was started by placing the bundles in water. If running water was available, then four days was usually enough, but standing water needed longer. Then the bundles were stood upright in the open for a long period. After this treatment the fibres were separated, sorted for length and dried. To ensure that the fibres were clean, straight and parallel they were combed out, a process known as hackling or heckling.

Hackling was often done by women. The bundles of fibres were drawn through a series of steel pins set in wooden blocks, known as hackling boards. Once hackled, the bundles were referred to as streaks, and these streaks were spun first into yarns, then strands, and finally into rope. The roper took a streak of hemp round his waist with the ends at the back. It was drawn out from the centre of the streak at the front, a small loop first being picked out and hung onto one of the hooks of the spinning wheel. The spinner walked backwards down the length of the walk as the yarn was spun up by the revolving hook, feeding out the hemp, and throwing it over the stakes when it was in danger of dropping to the floor. An experienced roper could spin a thousand feet of evenly twisted yarn in twelve minutes. The wheel was usually turned by a boy, who had to try to maintain an even speed on the wheel throughout the spinning, and the roper had to ensure that the yarn was smooth and even as he drew it out of the streak.

Supports known usually as stakes were placed throughout the length of the ropewalk at intervals of a few yards and the yarns were thrown over these as spinning progressed. Grit in the fibres of a rope could be disastrous, and there was usually plenty of it on the floors of some of the more primitive walks.

Figure 75(a) An Egyptian illustration, which is believed to depict ropemaking with flax. We must allow for a certain amount of artistic licence, and no doubt the length being twisted up is greatly shortened in the drawing. The strands, if such they can be called, are in the form

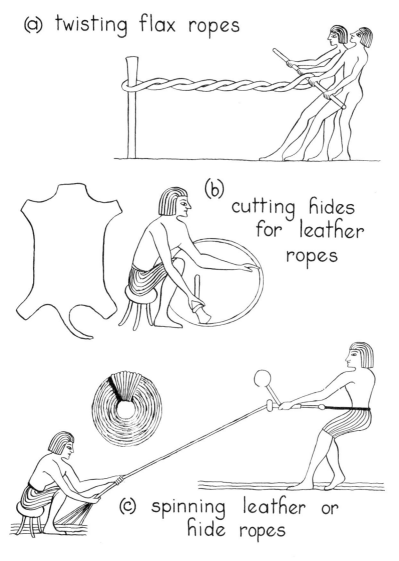

Figure 75 Egyptian ropers

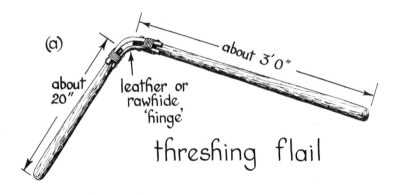

(a)

about 20"

leather or rawhide 'hinge'

about 3' 0"

threshing flail

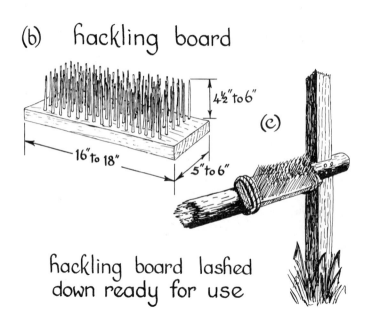

(b) hackling board

4½" to 6"

16" to 18"

5" to 6"

(c)

hackling board lashed down ready for use

Figure 76   Hemp preparation

of a loop, and I know of no illustration to show how these were made. Since they do not appear to have any reverse turns, one wonders how the rope would have held in its lay.

Figures 75(b) and (c)   These show the making of ropes from hides, which could have been either raw or tanned, most probably the former. The hides were cut into long single strands by working them round against a knife. It is apparent from the drawing that the knife is being held in one place rather than moved round the edge of the hide. The spinning is being done with what appears to be a tube with a rotating weight which twists the hide strips into a rope. The hide strips seem to be laid out in rows on the floor, from which they were picked up and controlled in spinning by one of the ropers. The process is in some ways the reverse of later practice, in that the spinning device is moving backwards, not the source of the material. Also shown is a completed coil of the rope.

Figure 76(a)   The common flail used not only for threshing out hemp seed, but also for threshing corn. The longer wooden part was the handle, and its use was something of an acquired knack. The beginner usually gave up with a painfully bruised back from the overswing of the swingel. Most of the examples I know of are from the threshing floors on farms, but since the growing of hemp was done on farms, the flail used was no different.

Figures 76(b) and (c)   Hackling boards, which came in a series of grades, in which the pins became progressively finer and set closer together, so that by the time the hemp had passed through the whole series it was as fine and straight as it could be. The boards were either lashed down to a convenient beam, as in (c), or a series was screwed down to a hackling bench. In this case the full range of boards would be used, set up in order along the bench, and the hemp was worked along the length of it. The finest of the hackle boards was known as a clearer, though sometimes this term meant a similar tool that was much finer than a hackle board and fitted with a handle. An alternative name for the hackle board was hatchell.

Figure 77(a)   Part of a ropewalk of about 1800, with two yarns being wound up from the stakes on to a reel. The spinning gear is not shown.
Figure 77(b)   A nineteenth-century ropewalk with two yarns being spun up at once using the type of spinning wheel sometimes called a table wheel. This particular one had seven hooks, though the standard towards the end of the eighteenth century seems to have been six, each with a separate driving belt. The hooks, or whirls, could be hooked up by the single driving belt in various combinations on the later version of the table wheel.

(a) ropewalk, circa 1800, from a contemporary aquatint

(b) spinning in a mid~19th.century ropewalk

Figure 77 Rope walks

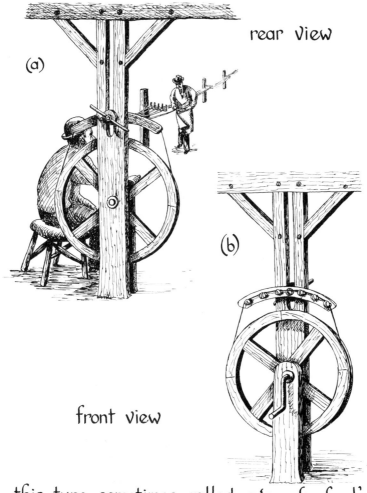

rear view

(a)

(b)

front view

this type sometimes called a 'crank wheel'

Figure 78   The spinning wheel

Figures 78(a) and (b)   Show a common type of spinning wheel which also went by the name of crank wheel. This was set up in a stout pillar in the fore end of the walk, and the belt could be tensioned by sliding the whirl carrier up or down the slot in the post. This illustration also shows a yarn being spun, and completed yarns on the stakes. The ends of the yarns were held out taut on an iron peg stake until they could be wound on to reels.

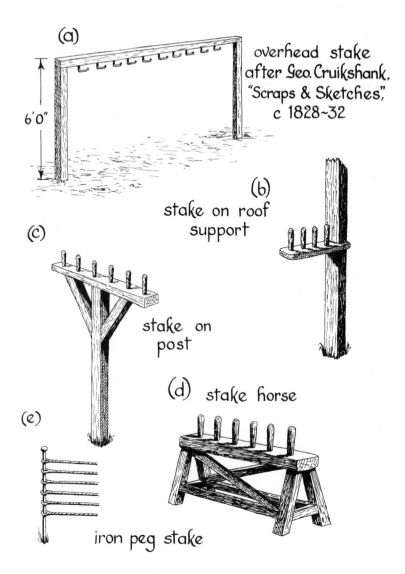

(a) overhead stake
after Geo. Cruikshank,
"Scraps & Sketches",
c 1828~32

6'0"

(b)
stake on roof
support

(c)
stake on
post

(d) stake horse

(e)
iron peg stake

Figure 79 Stakes

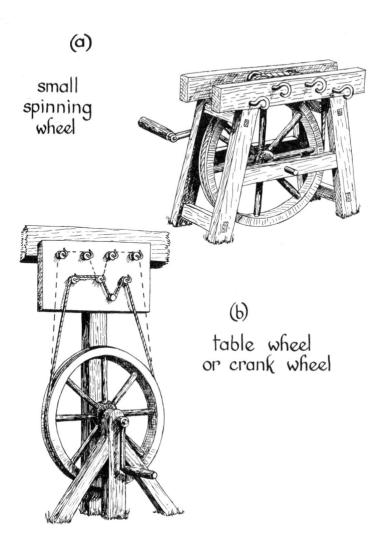

(a)

small
spinning
wheel

(b)

table wheel
or crank wheel

Figure 80   Wheels

Figures 79(a), (b), (c) and (d)   Various forms of stake used to support the yarns while being spun, and before winding on to reels. That in (a) was an overhead type, but the others were generally spaced out along the side of the walk. As the spinner passed each one he tossed the yarn into one of the spaces.

Figure 79(e)   One of the iron peg stakes used to peg out the ends of the yarns before they were wound up. These were not always used, for some walks had reels set up next to the wheel for winding up each yarn as it was completed.

Figures 80(a) and (b)   Two more versions of the spinning wheel which were used. The low type in (a) was more common in inland walks than coastal ones. The table wheel, (b), was widely used in both coastal and inland walks.

Figures 81(a) and (b)   Iron spinning wheels, which seem always to have been called 'jacks'. They were apparently an invention of the nineteenth century, and I have not been able to find any earlier evidence of their use. The light pattern, in (a), was usually bolted to either a heavy plank or a wooden frame. The heavy pattern, in (b), appears to have been a naval dockyard style, the hooks or whirls only engaging with the large gear when under tension.

Figures 82(a) and (b)   Two typical set-ups. Figure 82(a) shows a variation of the heavy iron jack bolted to a wooden frame. In (b) a light jack is bolted to a frame for spinning, and a reel is set up alongside for winding in the spun yarns. Four yarns could be spun at the same time on the jack, and a second hand would be kept standing by to unhook them as they were finished and wind them in on the reel while the spinners walked back up the walk holding the ends and keeping a tension on the yarns. Meanwhile a fresh set of spinners would have hooked up and started spinning four more sets of yarns.

Figures 83(a), (b) and (c)   Some of the forms of winding reels used. That in (c) is a heavy style, used to hold the strands, made up from a large number of yarns, before they in turn were laid up into the final rope.

Figures 84(a), (b) and (c)   Examples of sledges or drags which were used in spinning yarns into strands and laying up strands into rope.

208

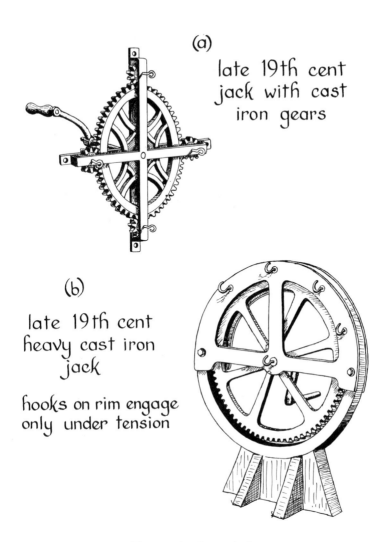

(a)
late 19th cent
jack with cast
iron gears

(b)
late 19th cent
heavy cast iron
jack

hooks on rim engage
only under tension

Figure 81   Rope jacks

(a)

framed
heavy jack

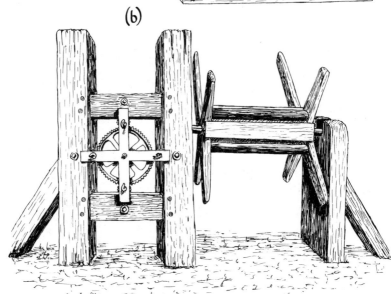

(b)

combined jack and reel set-up

Figure 82

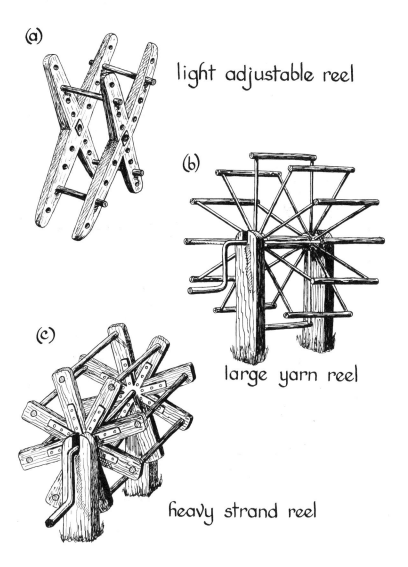

(a)

light adjustable reel

(b)

large yarn reel

(c)

heavy strand reel

Figure 83   Winding reels

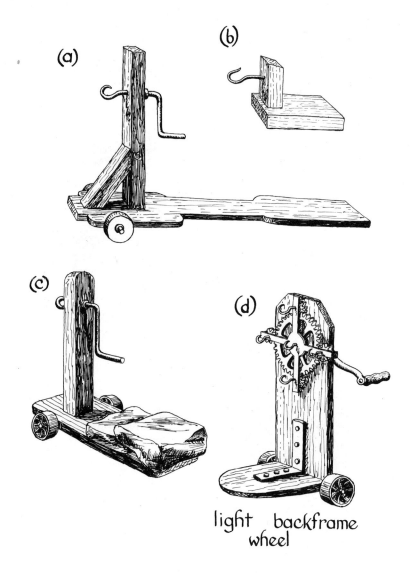

light backframe
wheel

Figure 84   Sledges

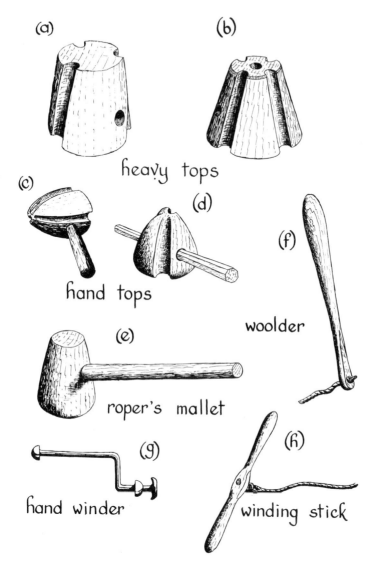

(a) (b)

heavy tops

(c)

(d)

hand tops

(f)

woolder

(e)

roper's mallet

(g)

hand winder

(h)

winding stick

Figure 85

The turning of three strands—each on a separate hook of a crank or table wheel, but with the other ends hooked to a common rotating hook —causes them to wind up together, but this needed to be controlled. The sledge was weighted to maintain tension as the winding-up took place, and the handle might be either lashed down to prevent it turning, or turned gently by hand to aid the winding of the strands.

Figure 84(d)   A backframe wheel, which could be used as a sledge or, using at least three of the hooks, used for hardening up strands from yarns. Some versions were much larger than the light one shown, which is fitted with a small jack. Large backframe wheels could be 4–5ft in diameter, mounted on a four-wheeled truck made from a 3in plank 11–13in wide and about 9ft long.

Figures 85(a), (b), (c) and (d)   These show roper's tops, which were used for closing a rope. As the strands were twisted up the top con-trolled the rate and tightness of the twist, guiding the strands evenly together. The two heavier ones, (a) and (b), were used on a top cart, (b) having a central bore for inserting a core in certain types of rope. The hand tops in (c) and (d) were for smaller ropes.

Figures 85(e), (f), (g) and (h)   These illustrate other aids to laying up or closing rope. The lay could be hardened with the mallet, (e), while the woolder, (f), was used to wind the rope tighter. The woolder was of wood, some 3ft long and 4in in circumference, with a strop of rope yarn fastened through a hole in one end. The strop was fastened on to the rope and the woolder twisted round to aid the closing of the rope. There were both single-handed and double-handed sizes.

Figures 85(g) and (h)   The hand winder and the winding stick were two more implements used to assist the winding of rope. The hand winder was used especially for making twines.

Figure 86   One method employed for laying strands into rope. The weighted sledge is at the outer end of the strands, and the top is in place. The strands are all attached to a wheel at the other end, then pass through a register plate, which is firmly fastened to an upright post. This was to prevent the strands touching and winding-up on the wrong side of the top.

Figures 87(a) and (b)   Two more varieties of heavy top used with top carts. Some were tapered almost to a point, others were shaped like a

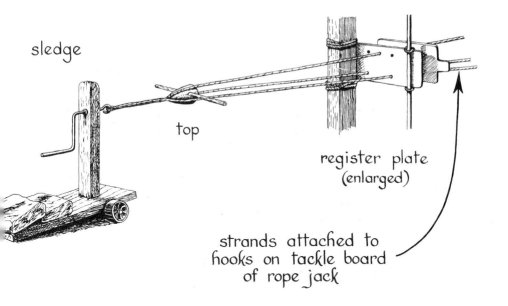

sledge

top

register plate
(enlarged)

strands attached to
hooks on tackle board
of rope jack

Figure 86   Laying strands

bullet or a truncated cone. All had grooves for the strands and holes to take the staff or staves, which were spars about 6–8ft long, $2\frac{1}{2}$–5in in diameter, and in the case of a staff for use with a hand top it could have a wheel fitted at the lower end to run along the ground as the rope closed.

Figures 87(c) and (d)   Typical topcarts, the first being an eighteenth-century style using a Spanish windlass tightened by spars to slow down the movement. The second is a much later design running on rails, and weighted with blocks of pig iron. With very heavy hawsers it could take as many as eighty men to handle the laying up.

Figures 88(a) and (b)   Two different sizes of tar kettles or coppers through which ropes were drawn to coat them with tar. Sometimes a complete rope was drawn through the hot tar, at others the strands or even the yarns were so treated. About the end of the eighteenth century a large tar kettle would hold from ten to twenty barrels of tar. The copper was firmly set in strong stonework or brickwork, with a firegrate and a chimney. The rope was drawn through the tar by a capstan or crab.

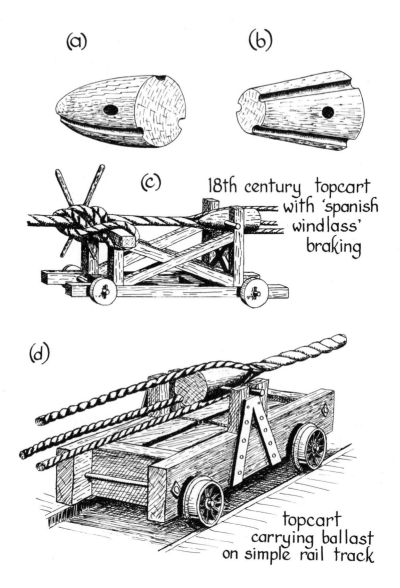

(a)

(b)

(c) 18th century topcart
with 'spanish
windlass'
braking

(d)

topcart
carrying ballast
on simple rail track

Figure 87   Tops and topcarts

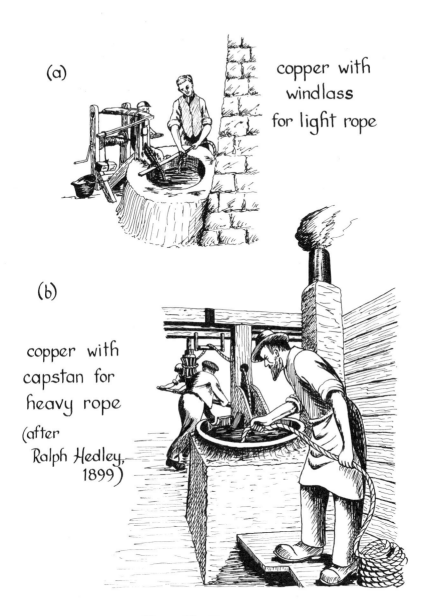

(a)

copper with
windlass
for light rope

(b)

copper with
capstan for
heavy rope
(after
Ralph Hedley,
1899)

Figure 88   Tar coppers

There were a few other tools used in ropemaking which I have not illustrated. Fids, similar to those used by riggers and sailmakers, in sizes from eight inches to twenty inches long, were found in the ropewalk, and iron marline spikes from eight to sixteen inches long. The loper was used for laying up lines, and had two iron swivel hooks, one at each end, running in a brass box. It was worked by the foreturn from the wheel at the head of the walk, but exactly how it was used I have not been able to discover. Pieces of mail (flat steel chainwork fastened to a piece of leather) were used in some walks for rubbing loose hemp off white cordage. When laying up heavy ropes extra weight might be added to the sledge in the form of a drag, which was fastened to the after end. It seems to have taken the form of an additional sledge with weights. Larger ropewalks around 1800 used what were known as press-barrels as weights on the sledge itself. These were old tar barrels filled with clay. They could be used on either the sledge or the drag, or both.

7

THE BLOCK, SPAR AND PUMP MAKER

The decline of the blockmaking aspect of the block, spar and pump maker's trade (when the products of the semi-mechanical blockmills at Southampton and Plymouth, and later elsewhere, flooded onto the commercial markets) has already been mentioned. Until then the greater part of the trade was employed in block and spar making alone, but gradually the transfer to more and more pump making, and even wooden pipe making, took place. The village carpenter was usually the man responsible for water pipes and the barrels of wooden village pumps, though these gave way fairly early to lead and later cast iron. But in the coastal districts the block maker was usually called in. Ships' pumps were of wood for a very long time after metal had been adopted on land, being made well into the twentieth century. There was also a range of special sizes and types of block which the blockmills could not handle economically, and these continued to be made by hand.

Because of the early decline of hand block making, comparatively few tools have survived, but those shown here probably reflect the greater part of the specialised collection to be found in a traditional block shop. These fall into three separate groups, one for each of the principal sections of the craft, but I have treated them as all belonging to the one tradesman, as indeed they did. The first of the illustrations shows the parts of a block, other than the rope or metal strap or strop, which may help to make clear the various stages involved.

Figure 89   The principal parts of the common block, with its shell, sheave and pin. Below this four sketches show the stages in cutting out the shell itself. Elm was usually chosen for its tough grain and durability in wet conditions. The sheave was usually of lignum vitae, but since for a very long time during the late-eighteenth and early-nineteenth centuries supplies of lignum vitae were under the control of the Taylor blockmaking mills at Southampton, some other material must have been in use. This also applies to blocks made before the introduction of lignum vitae, a date which I have not been able to discover.

Figures 90(a) and (b)   The block maker's holdfast bench and a typical holdfast or grip. The bench was made from an elm plank, about 3in thick, and had two uprights of 3in-square timber set within 4in of one end. The iron holdfast was driven down to clamp the wood being sawn or trimmed. The holdfast could be in several sizes, from about 15in up to 30in long, made from round bar which in turn could be from $\frac{1}{2}$in to 1$\frac{1}{2}$in in diameter. The longer straight part was known as the foot, and the shorter part with a flattened end to grip the wood was the head. I get the impression that each block shop could have either a series of holdfast benches, each with a different size of hole and holdfast, or one bench with a series of different holes.

Figure 90(c)   The block maker's brake, which was used to grip blocks while the holes were bored in them. The gripping lever had a pin set in it which could be placed in any one of a series of holes to suit the size of block.

Figure 90(d)   A clave, or block maker's stool, was used in shaping out the swallow of the block from the two bored holes. The blocks were held in place by large wedges and chocks of a suitable size.

Figure 91(a)   A block maker's burr, or squaring chisel, used for squaring out the corners of the swallow. It was a socketed tool, with an iron-bound top.

Figure 91(b)   The maul or mallet used in the trade.

Figures 91(c) and (d)   Two versions of bit used in blockmaking. They are rather shorter than those usual in the maritime trades. The brace was the normal type used by shipwrights and carpenters.

Figure 91(e)   The stock shave was for shaping the wooden blanks. It was also used by clogmakers and some other country craftsmen.

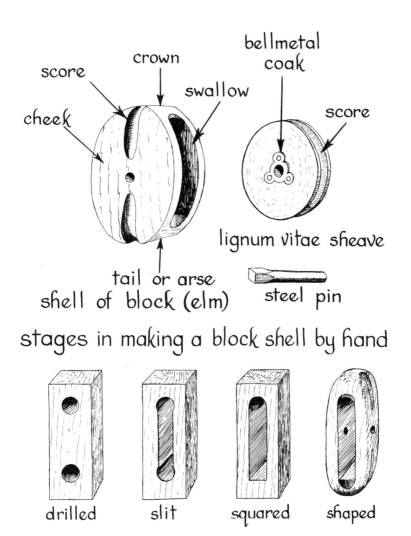

score

crown

bellmetal
coak

cheek

swallow

score

lignum vitae sheave

tail or arse

steel pin

shell of block (elm)

stages in making a block shell by hand

drilled

slit

squared

shaped

Figure 89   Parts of a block

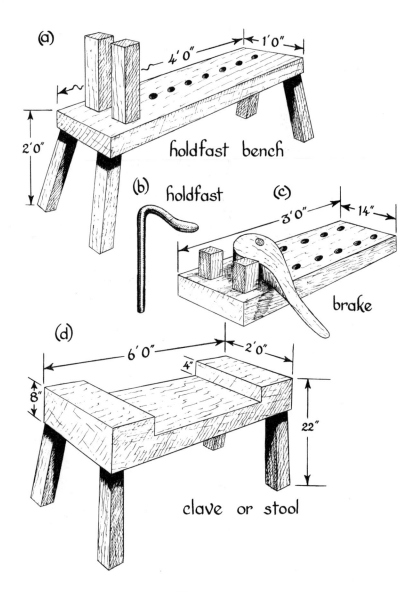

(a)

4'0"

1'0"

2'0"

holdfast bench

(b) holdfast

(c)

3'0"

14"

brake

(d)

6'0"

2'0"

4"

8"

22"

clave or stool

Figure 90

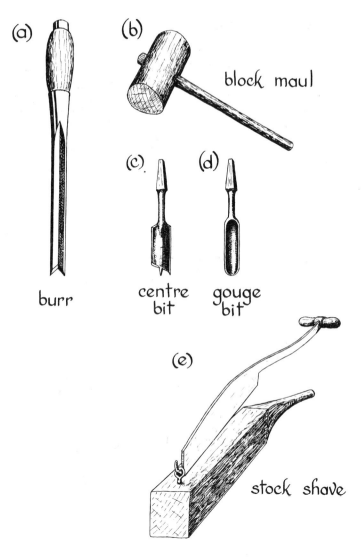

(a)

burr

(b)

block maul

(c)

centre bit

(d)

gouge bit

(e)

stock shave

Figure 91

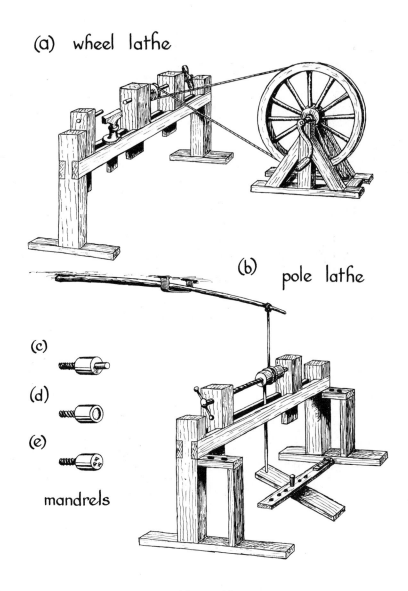

(a) wheel lathe

(b) pole lathe

(c)

(d)

(e)

mandrels

Figure 92

Figure 92(a)   A wheel lathe for turning sheaves. In this case it was turned by a lad on the wheel, which drove the lathe by a rope belt. The upright posts set between the plank lathe bed were known as puppets, and could be adjusted as needed.

Figure 92(b)   A more primitive lathe, a type known in the Iron Age in Britain, but which was nevertheless very effective for wood turning. The power source was a springy pole to which a rope was attached, working in opposition to a primitive treadle. The rope was wound round a spindle, and the lathe rotated in both directions, though the turning itself was only done on the correct rotation—towards the chisel edge.

Figures 92(c), (d) and (e)   Lathe mandrels used in the pole lathe to hold the work in place. Unfortunately I have not been able to find any of the tools used for turning sheaves, though they may very well have been of the usual turner's style.

Figure 93   Methods used in marking out a mast or spar from the squared-off log. There were several ways of marking out a mast, which is tapered from heel to truck. (In the case of a spar for a square sail, the taper runs from near the centre to the two ends.) The log was first squared, using the big blocking and mast axes shown under the shipwright's tools in Figure 29 I. One of the two principal methods of marking out consisted of striking a line down the centre of each side of the squared baulk, then measuring out from the line five twenty-fourths of the diameter of the proposed spar, or alternatively seven twenty-fourths from the outside edge. In each case a series of measurements were made and marked on. A line was then drawn through the marks from end to end. At the end of the baulk the lines would be extended and joined across the corners, forming an octagon. This octagonal section was then blocked out, throughout the whole length of the baulk. Another way was to draw crossed diagonals on the ends, as in (a), then strike arcs from the corners passing through the centre. Joining these points gave the octagon, and the extension of the octagonal corners down the length of the log to join at either end gave the lines to be worked to. This was only suitable for short spars, and the last two stages are shown in (b) and (c). Yet another way used either a two-foot single-fold rule or a simply-made siding gauge, as shown in (d) and (e). The rule was laid across the spar with the ends in line with the edges. Marks were then made at the 7in and 17in marks on the rule. Several points marked like this were then joined. The siding gauge was simply an

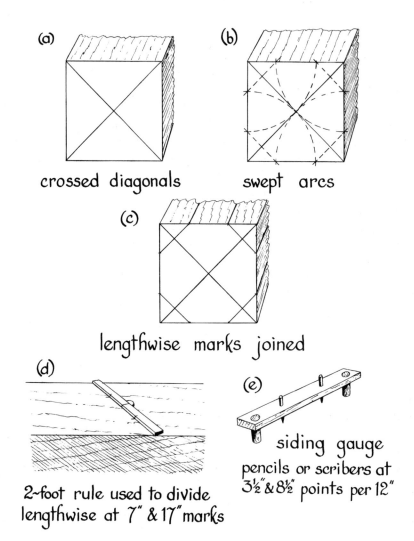

(a)

crossed diagonals

(b)

swept arcs

(c)

lengthwise marks joined

(d)

2-foot rule used to divide
lengthwise at 7" & 17" marks

(e)

siding gauge
pencils or scribers at
3½" & 8½" points per 12"

Figure 93

adaptation of the rule, with either two pencils or two scribers set through it at points which were $3\frac{1}{2}$in and $8\frac{1}{2}$in in every foot of length between the two guide posts. This was simply slid along the spar to give the lengthwise lines, the guide posts being kept tight to each side the whole way. Whichever way was chosen, the process was known as eight-squaring, and in a large diameter spar the marks might be subdivided again to form sixteen-square. A special rule was made for mast makers, known, naturally, as a mast maker's rule, 36in or more in length. On the edges were marked, in addition to inches, the divisions for eight-squaring. One edge was marked *M* for middle line, the other *E* for marks to be set within the edge. Both were needed in case the piece of timber would not work square enough to gain the squares and angles. There was also a sliding rule, a form of the more modern slide-rule, about one foot long, with a slide on which were marked various dimensions and proportions. This somewhat scientific instrument was probably used in the larger yards, or perhaps it was an Admiralty innovation for the Royal Dockyards.

Figures 94(a) and (b) Two methods used in fastening various components of large masts together. The cross sett utilised two short spars, 4–6ft long, which were lashed round the two pieces to be joined. Wedges were then driven between the top spar or staff and one of the parts being joined to tighten it further. The barrel-screws, (b), also known as bed screws, were a more conventional vice type of tool, mainly used for the 'raising' of the heads of masts, and for fixing trestle trees. The whole thing was made of elm, with two puppets or heavy screws, about 4ft 9in long. The heads might be round or octagonal, iron hooped to prevent splitting, with holes to take either long iron pins or stout wooden spikes. The width of the bed was three times the diameter of the screw; it was as thick as the diameter of the screw, and 6ft long. Six bolts were driven through the bed and clenched over iron rings to prevent splitting, and handholds were morticed into the sides and ends. The sole was about half of the thickness of the bed, sometimes reinforced with an iron plate let into each end with an iron sprig working on the heel of the puppet.
Figure 94(c) An eighteenth-century handscrew. We might today call it a jack—it was used for raising heavy mast parts—but in the words of David Steel in 1794 it was 'sometimes falsely called a jack.' Usage has defeated Steel, and jack it would surely be today. It consisted of a box of elm containing cast iron gears working on a rack, and a lock which

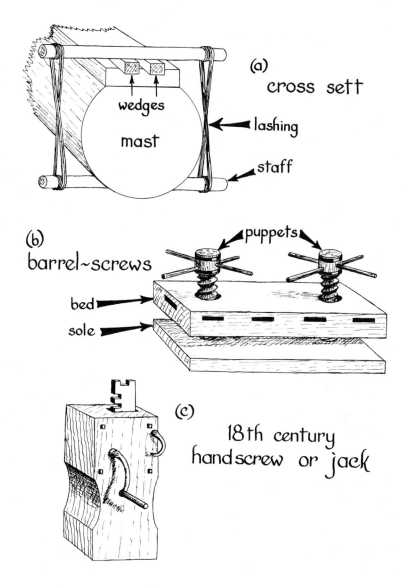

(a) cross sett

wedges

mast

lashing

staff

(b)
barrel~screws

puppets

bed

sole

(c)
18th century
handscrew or jack

Figure 94

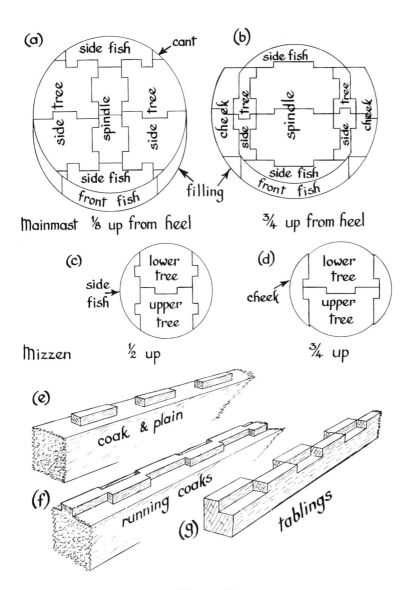

(a) side fish, cant, side tree, spindle, side tree, side fish, front fish, filling

Mainmast ⅛ up from heel

(b) side fish, cheek, side tree, side, spindle, tree, side, cheek, side fish, front fish, filling

¾ up from heel

(c) lower tree, upper tree, side fish

Mizzen ½ up

(d) lower tree, upper tree, cheek

¾ up

(e) coak & plain

(f) running coaks

(g) tablings

Figure 95

was thrown by the short curved handle. It could be single-power or double-power, according to the gearing.

Figure 95 The making of large masts involved a great deal of construction, and I have drawn typical sections through large and small masts of the late eighteenth century. The mizzen mast of a large ship would be too big for many of the smaller ships, for which masts were usually made from a single tree or baulk, but these large items were built of many parts, all carefully shaped and fitted together. The forms of jointing used are shown in (e), (f) and (g). There were also through-boltings, as in the spindle of a mast, which was usually of two pieces, tapering from heel to top, coaked into each other in the middle, and through-bolted at 5ft intervals. (Coaking was the method of transverse jointing in a mast. It usually consisted of a series of square teeth cut in each part, then closed together.) The whole mast was woolded together with rope wooldings of thirteen close turns each, each turn being held by woolding nails with leather under their heads to prevent them cutting the rope. Iron bands or hoops were also fitted, but these were under parts of the mast—the front fish or paunch—and the wooldings were spaced out between the bands.

Figure 96 This illustrates the method of boring out a pump barrel, for which elm was almost always used. Not only does it possess a very strong grain, and is resistant to water immersion, but the tree often suffers from a heart rot—hence the tendency to be blown down in gales—which makes it easier to bore out. The chosen piece was dogged down on chocks or blocks at a suitable angle, and a trestle placed to steady the lead-in of the long augers. The first cut was made with an auger, usually with its own long shaft, up to 14ft long, then the hole was opened out with larger and larger reamers until the desired size was achieved.

Figures 97(a), (b), (c), (d) and (e) Typical pump and water pipe boring tools. The auger in (a) would be used to open the first hole. It would be followed by reamers of the kind in (b) up to the larger sizes as in (e). These were all used in a boring bar, in which the bit was secured by a key. The reamers had a variety of local names, the usual being 'spoons', and one Scottish manufacturer described his exhibits in the Great Exhibition of 1851 as 'scollops' or reamers. The larger sizes of reamer had two holes in the non-cutting edge, to which pads of iron

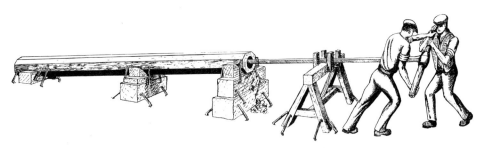

Figure 96   Boring out a pump barrel

could be added by bolts to increase the diameter cut. The two augers in (c) and (d) were varieties of the augers used to start the bore.

Figure 97(f)   Another auger that might just be found among the tools of a pump maker, though it is rather an old style. It is a hook auger, again with its own haft, though its shape is such that it was more a reamer, and could only be used on a pre-bored hole. The hook was designed to take a rope by which the tool could be pulled through in addition to being driven through by the haft.

Figure 97(g)   The boring bar used for pump reamers. As already stated, it could be up to 14ft long, the average being 12ft.

The block, spar and pump maker used some other tools, apart from the turning chisels mentioned. He was adept with the adze, and seems to have used the shipwright's version of it, together with the shipwright's range of axes, augers and stocks. The common draw-knife was used to shave off the angles left by axes, adzes and planes on the mast sides, and some very large compasses and callipers were used. Some of these had legs nearly 5ft long. Planes of various types were used, especially the larger sizes of jack planes and the varieties made with curving soles (see Chapter 4). A plumb bob and line were part of his tool kit, and a pin maul. A racing knife was a small knife used for marking lines with a cut—known as racing, whether done with a knife, points of a compass or any other point. Long lines were marked out with a ram-line, which was thick twine, fastened down at one end, hauled very tight and straight, and fastened down at the other. Bevel gauges and try squares and most of the normal chisels and slices were also found in the block maker's tool chest. In many of the smaller yards one of the shipwrights often specialised in making spars, especially as the trade of block making tailed off. Shipwrights seem to have been expected to know how to make masts of most kinds.

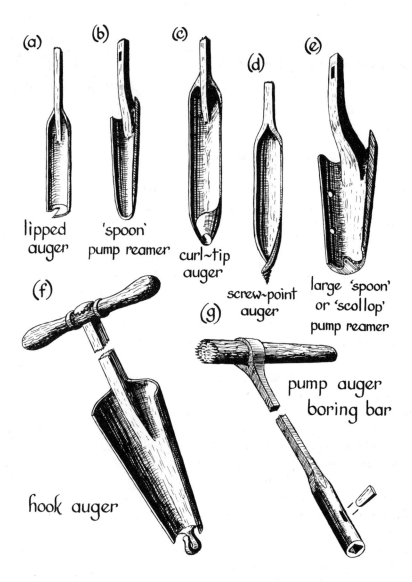

(a) lipped auger

(b) 'spoon' pump reamer

(c) curl~tip auger

(d) screw~point auger

(e) large 'spoon' or 'scollop' pump reamer

(f) hook auger

(g) pump auger boring bar

Figure 97   Augers and reamers

8

THE BLACKSMITH, SHIPSMITH AND ANCHORSMITH

Strictly speaking the word 'smith' implied that the craftsman referred to was a worker in metal. It was usual to qualify the name—blacksmith for an iron worker; coppersmith, tinsmith for sheet metal worker; silversmith, goldsmith and so on. But over the many centuries that metal working has been carried on men began to specialise not only in a particular metal, but in a specific type of product. Thus by the middle of the nineteenth century those blacksmiths specialising in ship's fittings frequently termed themselves shipsmiths, especially in the smaller (though not the very small) centres. It may be that this expression stayed longer in some places than others, but the term anchorsmith was pretty widespread. In view of the heaviness of the work, it is not in the least surprising that this became a specialised branch of smithing. The term trawlersmith, however, had a rather more limited application. It was used in those places where trawling for fish had become a major industry, and the building of trawlers was a large part of the work of the local maritime trades. The British trawling industry is today a vast business, but its origins were mainly in the eighteenth century in the port of Brixham, in South Devon, and it was in those ports to which the Brixham men carried their craft, and where trawlers were subsequently built, that the trawlersmith could be found. (Brixham itself, of course, and Ramsgate, Lowestoft, Hull, Grimsby, Plymouth, Tenby, Milford Haven and Ringsand, near Dublin, were some of the trawling centres.) The trawlersmith not only made the fittings for trawlers, but also the iron trawl heads used on the old-style beam trawls, which were the mainstay of the trawling industry in the days of sail.

Figure 98(a) Hero's design for a tilt hammer, dating from about 150BC, though the design as interpreted in 1693 suggests it was some form of mass execution machine. Even in the second century BC men were thinking in terms of some form of power for heavy hammering.

Figures 98 (b) and (c) These show the basic difference in the operation of the two most-used forms of what might be termed mechanical hammers. Before Nasmyth's invention of the steam hammer in the fourth decade of the nineteenth century, water-powered trip and tilt hammers were the main tools in heavy forging. Many ingenious tools were devised by the smiths to help them with their work.

Figure 99 The eighteenth-century version of Nasmyth's later invention, the 'Hercules'. The fall of the weight or hammer was guided by rollers, and a single control rod operated by the senior smith gave closer guidance. A team of labourers hauled on the tails to lift the 400-pound weight, and its release had to be carefully synchronised to avoid accidents. When not in use the weight was held by a stout pin through the suspension rod and a pair of iron supports on the beam above. My illustration shows these much too light to carry out their function, but otherwise most of the detail would be obscured. For this reason only two of the four guide rollers are shown in place.

opposite (above) The trawler *Markum* under construction, Brixham, 1910
(below) The trawler *Markum* ready for launching

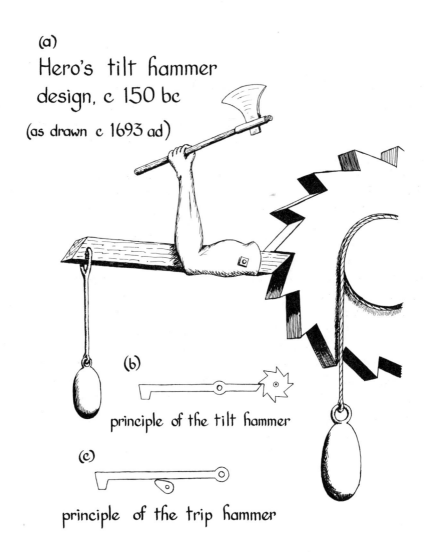

(a)
Hero's tilt hammer
design, c 150 bc

(as drawn c 1693 ad)

(b)

principle of the tilt hammer

(c)

principle of the trip hammer

Figure 98 'Power' hammers

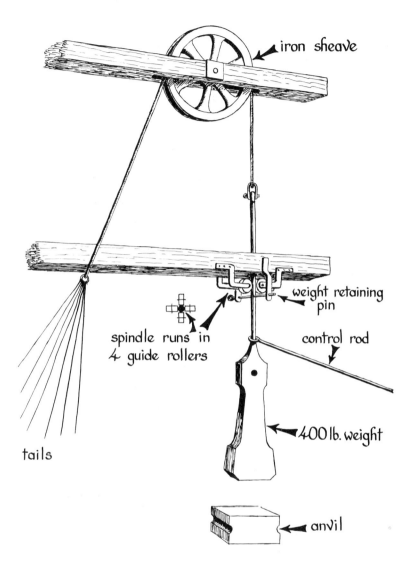

iron sheave

weight retaining pin

spindle runs in 4 guide rollers

control rod

400 lb. weight

tails

anvil

Figure 99   The 'hercules', 18th century

(a)

(b)

Figure 100   Heavy forges of the late 18th century

Figure 100   Two examples of heavy forges of the late eighteenth century. Various forms of anvil are shown, and the enormous hand-operated bellows. Over the forges are simple cranes, consisting of vertical swivelling beams with strutted horizontal members, at the end of which are chains and hooks.

Figure 101(a)   Another of the simple aids devised to help the smith. The 'monkey' was a 200-pound weight suspended from a crane and swung sideways to hammer against the side of the metal being forged.
Figure 101(b)   A simple cutter used for cropping cold bars.

(a)

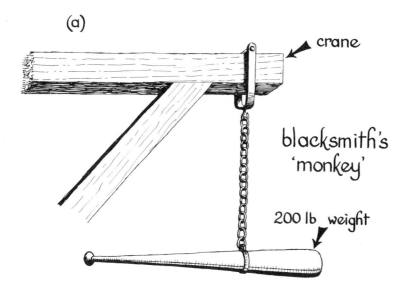

crane

blacksmith's
'monkey'

200 lb weight

(b) anvil cutter for cropping bars

struck here

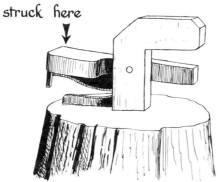

Figure 101   The smithy

Figure 102   Forging an anchor-stock, 1780

Figure 102   An anchor stock being forged using a trip hammer. The handling of the stock by six men and a crane is fairly clear. The master smith is controlling the hammer and guiding the movements of the stock by indicating to his men exactly where he wants it.

Figure 103   Various stages in the making of an anchor stock, and the use of the various porter bars for handling it. The anchor stock itself was forged from flat strips, welded under the hammer into a solid bar. The laminations can sometimes be seen in old anchors when corrosion along the strips has taken place.

Figure 104   This illustrates what is really only a typical example of the smaller forge used by blacksmiths. The essential hearth is there, with the air supply fed in from behind. Today the air is fed from a pneumatic service or compressed air system; some forges still have bellows, but even in the smallest forges the bellows have usually given way to small rotary fans. Round the rim of the hearth are iron bars to take tools such as tongs, and in the front part of it a quenching trough. On the hearth are the fire rake and flat shovel for tending the fire.

240

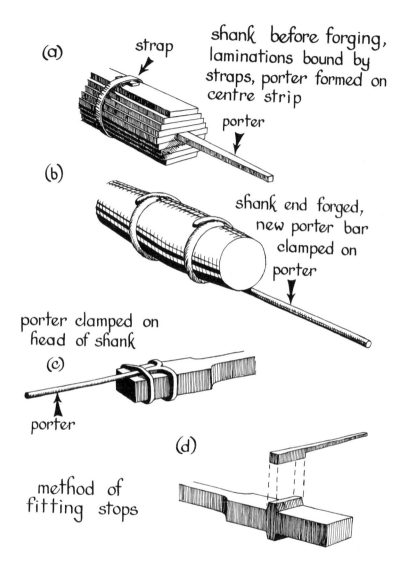

(a) strap shank before forging, laminations bound by straps, porter formed on centre strip

porter

(b) shank end forged, new porter bar clamped on porter

porter clamped on head of shank

(c) porter

method of fitting stops

(d)

Figure 103   Anchor-making

Figure 104   The forge

Figure 105   The anvil used for most forging work today, other than for very heavy work like anchor making. According to Pliny the anvil is supposed to have been invented by Cinyra of Cyprus, but it was probably much older. There has been very little change in the basic design of the anvil since Greek and Roman times, as with the hammer.

Figure 106(a)   A typical form of the blacksmith's bellows. The back of the forge is fitted with an inlet lined with a tue iron which leads the air to the right place. The 'spout' of the bellows fitted into this. The cowhorn tip to the operating lever is one of those traditional touches which have died out with the introduction of the rotary fan.
Figures 106(b) and (c)   The stake and the hardie, which fit into the stake hole or hardie hole in the anvil. The stake formed what was virtually a miniature anvil, and the hardie was used for cutting hot bars.

242

several patterns and sizes up
to about 3 cwt

face of blister steel
welded on

pritchel hole

table

stake or
hardie hole

bick or beak

face

wrought iron
body

throat

heel or
wedge

U~clips

tool
hangers

block

block is baulk or log set up to 4 feet in the ground

Figure 105 The anvil

(a) bellows

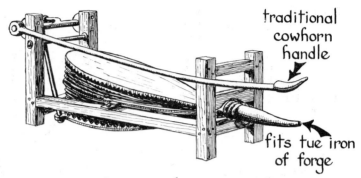

traditional
cowhorn
handle

fits tue iron
of forge

tools for the anvil

(b)

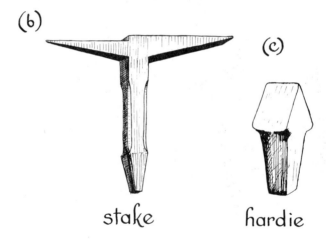

(c)

stake   hardie

Figure 106

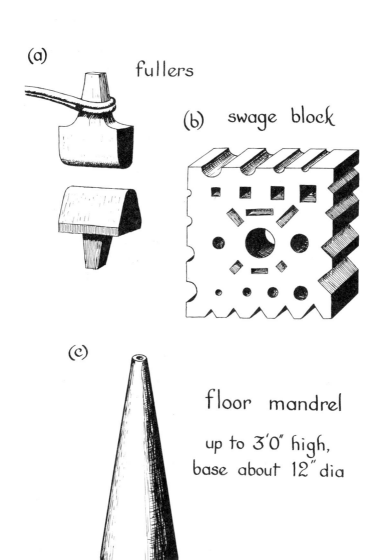

(a) fullers

(b) swage block

(c) floor mandrel

up to 3'0" high,
base about 12" dia

Figure 107

Figure 107(a)   A pair of fullers, both top and bottom parts. The bottom part was set in the anvil, and the upper part was used with a haft which at one time would have been of withy, but is now usually of round steel bar. Fullers were of various forms made to suit the shapes for which they might be required.

Figure 107(b)   A swage block, made of cast iron, which came with a cast iron stand in which it could be set upright on any of the four sides. It was used for shaping rounds and squares in the sides, and for shaping through the central holes.

Figure 107(c)   A floor mandrel, used in the making of hoops and bands.

Figures 108(a) and (b)   A pair of swages and a pair of fullers, to show the main distinction between these two rather similar tools. The swage forms a shape on the outside of the metal, while the fullers drive into the metal to form a hollow or groove.

Figures 108(c), (d) and (e)   Three more tools used with hafts, and struck by the hammer. The cold set was for cutting cold, the hot set for cutting hot, and the flatter for flattening.

Figures 109(a), (b) and (c)   The three most normal kinds of hammer found in the smithy. The ball pein is strictly an engineer's hammer, but it is in almost every smith's tool box. The cross pein and straight pein types are the most used by smiths, about two pounds in weight. A two-handed hammer was used by the smith's mate, known as the striker, for cutting and other work. It was called a backing hammer, and could be up to four pounds in weight. Sledges, as much as seven or twelve pounds, and in some heavy forges up to twenty pounds, with hickory hafts about three feet long, were also used.

Figures 110(a), (b), (c), (d), (e) and (f)   Tongs, another of the essential tools of the smith's craft, were made up by the smith to suit the particular work in which he specialised, though certain types such as the close tongs, flat tongs and side tongs were probably common to most if not all smithies. It is said that there were more varieties of tongs in a smithy than of any other tool, since they were often specially made for one particular job and kept in case of a future need.

Figure 111(a)   The leg vice common to most smithies. Again, it is really an engineer's tool, but then the smith was often the nearest approach to

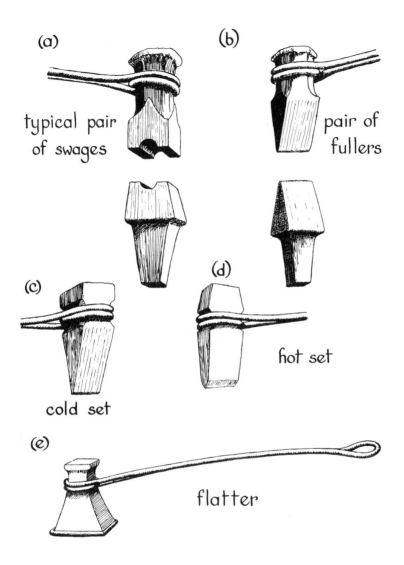

(a)

typical pair
of swages

(b)

pair of
fullers

(c)

cold set

(d)

hot set

(e)

flatter

Figure 108

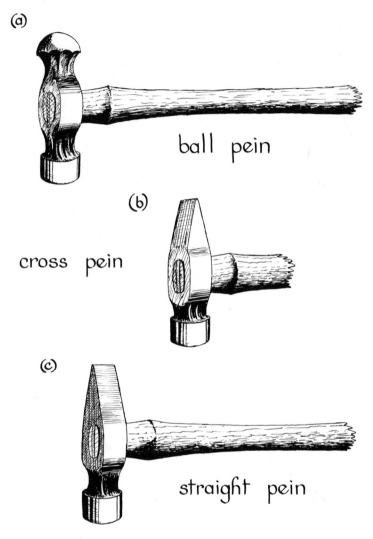

(a)

ball pein

(b)

cross pein

(c)

straight pein

Figure 109   Hammers

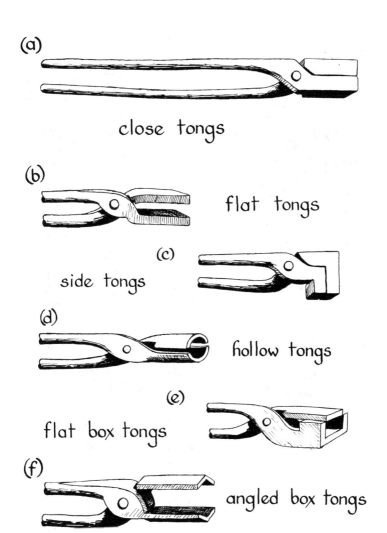

(a)

close tongs

(b)

flat tongs

(c)

side tongs

(d)

hollow tongs

(e)

flat box tongs

(f)

angled box tongs

Figure 110   Tongs

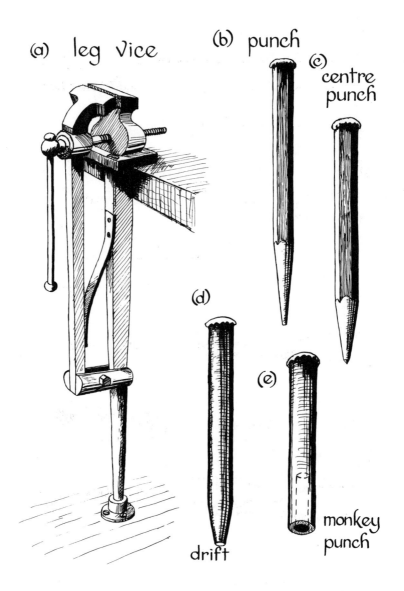

(a) leg vice

(b) punch

(c) centre punch

(d) drift

(e) monkey punch

Figure 111

Figure 112 Dumb striker

an engineer, perhaps for many miles, and he was called upon to do a wide variety of work.

Figures 111(b), (c) and (d) Forms of punch used by the smith, and common to most engineers and metal workers. The centre punch marks centres for drilling, outlines particular positions, and so on, and has a pointed end. The punch has a slightly squared end to make a flatter impression or to punch out small holes in thin metal. The drift is used either for driving in or driving out rivets, spindles and the like.

Figure 111(e) The monkey punch is a tool I have not found as a punch in any other trade, and appears to have been used for driving washers and plates over spindles.

Figure 112 A sketch of a dumb striker which once graced the smith's department at Palmer's Shipyard at Jarrow. The drawing is based closely on a sketch provided by Mr Ernest Gerrie, of Erith, Kent, who also described how it was used :

> In December 1917 I entered into employment with Palmer's Shipbuilding Co, Jarrow on Tyne, at the age of 14, and worked with the blacksmith as an odd job lad until I was 16 years old—when I commenced an apprenticeship.

251

It must be appreciated that Palmers at that time was a huge, self-contained shipbuilding concern, building merchant and naval vessels practically from raw materials, with blast furnaces, rolling mills, converting iron ore into steel ships.

This was the setting for the strange tool or apparatus. I remember the details quite well, because I was actually allowed to operate this formidable contraption on rare occasions.

Jack Slater, the operator, produced a fantastic number of 1 inch bolts daily on this machine—on a piece-work basis, which I believe was priced on a 'two-man' basis. He worked from 6am to 7pm and earned good wages. His performance, leaping up and down to produce the maximum power was quite fantastic, but this produced little comment from the other smiths, one of whom told me it was quite a common sight in the days of 'Wooden Ships and Iron Men'.

Mr Gerrie did not stay with the trade for long, and when he retired a few years ago he had been a Civil Servant for over thirty years. It is seldom that one finds a former craftsman articulate enough to be able to write as well as he did to me, and I consider myself lucky. I quote further from him on the method of making the bolts, with my notes interspersed :

The operator would spend some time cutting bars into the required lengths, using the machine and an anvil-chisel [or hardie], the bars being nicked around the circumference and broken by a tap on the anvil. Secondly the collars would be cut to length in a similar manner, then forged to the required shape [an open hexagon to make the bolt head]. Thirdly the collar was welded and shaped to the hexagonal form by placing in a bolster [in the block below the machine] and bringing the machine into operation. The whole of this process was carried out with one 'heat', and took about one minute each, to produce a strong and reliable bolt. They were threaded later and used mainly I believe by carpenters—working at that time on HMS *Dauntless*, which was completed in 1918.

As can be seen from the sketch, the striker was operated by the spring of a plank mounted above it, and brought down by the smith's foot. Although only used at Palmer's for producing bolts, in former times it could have been used for a number of other hammering tasks.

The smith used a few other tools in his work, such as compasses, dividers and the essential rule, made of brass—steel would soon blacken too much to be read. He also had a number of shaped bolsters, such as that used

252

with the dumb striker already discussed, to aid in forming shapes. Drifts, punches, cold chisels, files and rasps of different types and sizes all formed part of his equipment. Naturally enough the smith made a great many tools, particularly dies, formers and jigs devised for a multitude of purposes.

I have made no attempt to describe how the various smiths carried out their actual work. Even if I knew how, it would take volumes. But one important part of the smith's work, wherever he was, consisted of hardening and tempering iron and steel. For this he used the tank or trough on the front of the forge hearth, and sometimes special tanks of other fluids, oil and so on. The fluid itself for most purposes was basically water, and in some parts of Britain the concoction, often highly individual and 'secret', was known as 'bosh'. In yet another passage from Ernest Gerrie:

> Of course, individuality creeps in, and I well remember one old tool-fettler who urinated into his waterbutt or 'bosh' and swore that this imparted some special quality to the edges of his tools.
>
> Also another who used a 'secret' recipe for case-hardening. This was a foul-smelling concoction of old boot-leather, sulphur and other strange ingredients—but, of course, there may have been a scientific basis for his mixture.

Those words give a clue to the character of the master or journeyman smith who was an individualist, highly inventive and truly proud of his ancient craft. The odd one went to quite extraordinary lengths, such as the Torquay village blacksmith who, about 1820, built himself an iron boat for fishing among the rocks of the Torbay coastline. I think it must have been one of the first iron vessels built. The plating of this metal rowing boat must have been hammered out, possibly by hand. It lasted for several years, but was not greatly used, being very heavy for hauling up the beach.

9

OTHER TRADES IN THE MARITIME COMMUNITIES

Every maritime centre had a number of other tradesmen who were not necessarily only maritime craftsmen. It must be admitted that most of the tradesmen mentioned could turn their hands to other work, and indeed as the days of first the commercial sailing vessels and then wooden ships declined, and as machinery made easier and simpler the tasks that had once been laboriously carried out, many tradesmen were forced to diversify. Sailmakers became tentmakers, shipwrights became house-builders and carpenters, and so on. But coopers and basketmakers could be found in many other places besides the coastal towns. Every brewery had, and to some extent still has, its complement of coopers, and basket-makers were called for in almost every town and village community. There were also a few tasks carried out not so much by craftsmen as by labourers, but which called for specialised tools.

BARKING YARDS

In a port which specialised in fishing there were plenty of people who made nets, without being netmakers by profession, and certain men made the great wooden trawl beams—two young trees, roughly trimmed but with the bark still on, scarphed together end to end and bound in iron over the scarph—where there was a trawl fishery. In most fishing ports, too, there would be the barking yards. These were the places where the sails were tanned to preserve them. The yards themselves consisted of no more than a clear space on which to lay the sails flat, a large boiler of the concoction used, and a tall spar with a block and tackle for hoisting the sails up to dry. This work was also described on that 1958 tape recording (see p.195). The speakers are identified by the following initials:

WS—the late William Stokes
WSD—the late William Smerdon Dart
CA—the late Charles Ashford
JSC—J. Stanley Churchill
JEH—the author

WS :   Bark yards? Oh, yes, there used to be three bark yards, Furneaux's bark yard, Lake's and Drew's, two up Overgang and one over the Southern Quay. That was the bark yard. They used to get the sails in, of a dry day, bark 'em, hoist 'em up on a great big mast, dry, and take 'em aboard the boat the same day and bend 'em, what they used to call bendin' of 'em, ready for hoistin' of at any time they 'ad a mind to go to sea.

WSD :   And all their clothes would be red, all that colour [indicating the tanned sails of a model trawler], and a' course every owner 'ad 'is own pertic'ler shade, when they was boiling the stuff what they used to bark these sails. That was supposed to be—every barking yard 'ad 'is own secret formler [formula], as 'e called it. And there used to be a 'uge copper vat up in these barking yards, and so much tallow, so much water, ochre, oak bark, bring all this to the boil up there, and—er—

WS :   I remember a Brixham man fallin' in—

JSC :   Albert Boyne.

CA :   I've got up four o'clock in the morning and gone down to bark some sails with my father, and gone to me own job at six o'clock.

JEH :   I have heard that the sails used to have to be in by four o'clock in the morning to be done that day.

WS :   Oh, no, make your own time, book up your barking day with the person concerned, and then they had a great stick with great flaps of sailcloth, and they used to put it in great bark tubs—in, and slap it on and—the crews—

WSD :   The crews, more or less the owner and the crews 'ad to provide the labour.

WS :   Oh, they done it theyself, oh, yes.

WSD :   The barking yard owner, 'e only provided the yard and the mixture.

CA :   O' course some one 'ad to start early in the mornin', 'cos some days there was three or four ships to bark.

WS :   Oh, yes.

WSD :   Course the thing 'ad to be boilin' overnight, huge cauldron of it.

Barking, of course, takes its name from the fact that powdered oak bark was the principal constituent of the mixture applied to the sails, regardless of how secret the 'formler' might be. Linseed oil was another ingredient sometimes used. About 1900 the oak bark started to be replaced by an imported tanning agent known in some ports as kutch. Kutch or catechu was made from several eastern tree barks, though most of the fishermen thought it came from India. The mast was usually an old ship's mast, set up in the yard. Naturally it had to be a taller mast than those of the sailing trawlers, and able to take the largest of the sails.

I have not been able to discover how much was charged by the bark yard proprietors for their service, but no doubt it was quite a lucrative little sideline. In each case at Brixham the yards were not the principal businesses of the proprietors, and it must be admitted that the British climate, even in Devon, would not allow the yards to be used on every day of the year. It may be thought that barking was a rather unproductive task for the fishermen, who took as their pay a share of the proceeds of the catch. Even though an essential job, it certainly was not very popular. But a sailing trawler needed a strong wind for trawling, and the weather which suited barking was quite unsuitable for the fishermen to go to sea. However, one cannot always judge the weather so exactly as to achieve the perfect timetable in such matters.

THE FIGURES

Figures 113(a), (b) and (c) Three forms of barking irons used to strip oak bark off the trees after they had been felled. The bark was split down with an axe and then lifted off in pieces with the irons which were worked under the bark to loosen it. The bark was carefully dried in stacks, and ground into a powder for use not only in barking sails but also for tanning leather. These irons seem to have been a fairly late introduction, the earlier tool having been a sharpened leg bone of a horse, which apparently was exactly the right shape.

Figure 113(d) The American equivalent of the irons combined in an axe, with a pronounced offset in the haft. No doubt some form of irons or even again the leg bone were used in American woods as well.

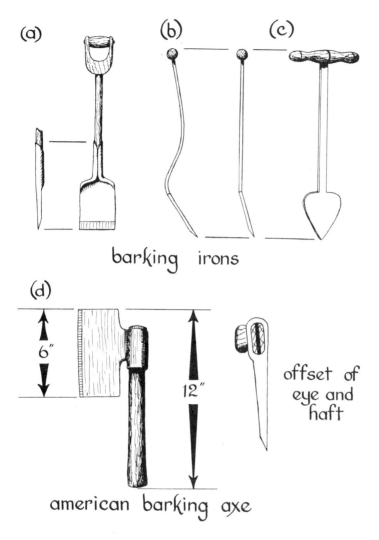

(a)

(b)

(c)

barking irons

(d)

6"

12"

offset of
eye and
haft

american barking axe

Figure 113   Barking tools

THE BASKETMAKER

The basketmaker was an important character in every maritime community. He made the range of maunds or baskets used in cargo handling; fish baskets, which went by a whole variety of names and were produced in just as wide a range of shapes and types; strainers for the bottom ends of the bilge pumps; special packing baskets for transporting things like china and glassware; lunch baskets; and, in some places, even lobster and crab pots, though generally these were made by the fishermen themselves. Since their products were rather short-lived the basketmakers usually had plenty of work, and many of them held positions of some importance in the smaller maritime communities. Just as the shipwright was known as a chippy, and the block maker as 'Blocky', so, too, the basketmaker had his nickname—'Twiggy'.

THE FIGURES

Figures 114(a), (b) and (c) Breaks, which were used for stripping the rind or bark off willow or osier to prepare it for working.

Figure 114(d) A heavier version of the break set in a wooden block. The basketmaker who worked mainly in osier was often known not as a basketmaker but as a rod-weaver.

Figure 114 (e) is a splitter set in a wooden block for splitting osiers, and is sometimes called an upright. It was of steel, sharpened on one edge, and the osiers were pulled past it.

Figures 115(a) and (b) Picking knives, used for trimming off ends on finished baskets.

Figure 115(c) A cleaving knife, used for splitting osier.

Figures 115(d) and (e) Shop knives, used for sharpening or pointing rods.

Figure 115(f) A pricker-up, used for turning or pricking up willow stakes after they had been set in the base. This tool may be modern. It appears in twentieth-century catalogues but I have not found it among the nineteenth-century tools used by the traditional basketmakers. This suggests it may have been a late introduction.

Figures 115(g), (h) and (i) Beating irons, which were used for beating down the weave into place. These are only three types, or examples, for yet again this is a tool which might be made up by the local blacksmith.

Figures 115(j), (k) and (l) Typical bodkins used to open the weave

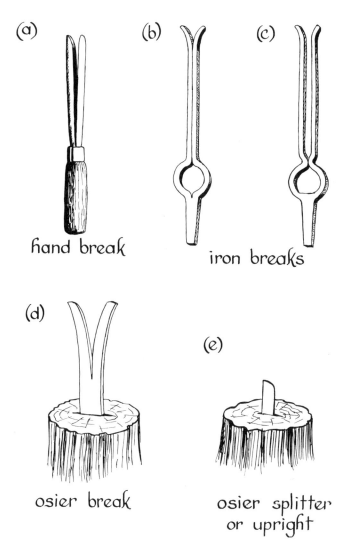

(a)

hand break

(b)

(c)

iron breaks

(d)

osier break

(e)

osier splitter
or upright

Figure 114   The basketmaker

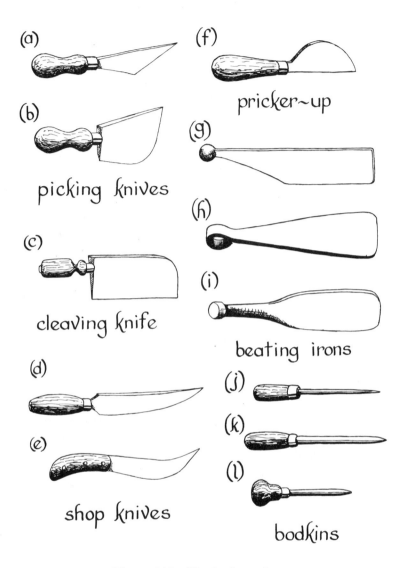

(a)

(f)

pricker~up

(b)

picking knives

(g)

(c)

(h)

cleaving knife

(i)

beating irons

(d)

(j)

(k)

(e)

(l)

shop knives

bodkins

Figure 115   The basketmaker

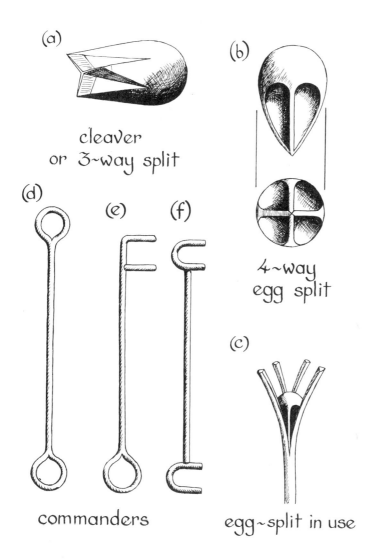

(a) cleaver or 3~way split

(b) 4~way egg split

(c) egg~split in use

(d) (e) (f) commanders

Figure 116   The basketmaker

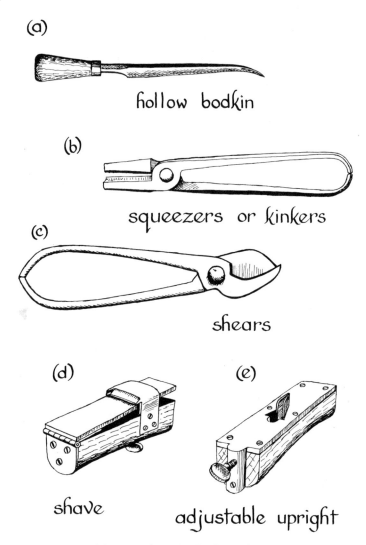

(a)

hollow bodkin

(b)

squeezers or kinkers

(c)

shears

(d)

shave

(e)

adjustable upright

Figure 117   The basketmaker

to insert rods. They might be made of iron, wood, antler or bone, and were not always fitted with handles.

Figures 116(a), (b) and (c)   Cleavers or splits, used to split the osier into three or four separate strips. The four-way split is commonly known as an egg-split, for obvious reasons, and is shown in use.

Figures 116(d), (e) and (f)   Commanders—iron bars designed to fit across the rising basketwork to keep the diameter correct.

Figure 117(a)   A hollow bodkin, which allowed a rod to be inserted through the groove when used in tight places.

Figure 117(b)   Kinkers, used to produce sharp bends in the rods without actually cutting them.

Figure 117(c)   Shears, used for cutting heavy rods, though most basketmakers preferred the knife for cutting.

Figure 117(d)   A shave, with an adjustable blade, for shaving down split osier into flat strands. This process removed the pith and produced a smooth, flat finish.

Figure 117(e)   Another splitting device, an adjustable upright, which could be varied to suit the rods.

The tools of the country basketmaker have been fairly well covered in a number of books, but one that does deserve mention is the old basketmaker's rule, a wooden yardstick marked out at $2\frac{1}{4}$in intervals by nails. These measurements were known as nails, but about 1860 or 1870 were replaced by the more usual inches. Most of the coastal workers used osier, but elsewhere both cane and osier (or willow) were used. It was considered unfair to ask a man to work both, since a man working willow and transferring to cane would have his hands rubbed raw inside a day.

THE COOPER

The cooper's trade is also of great antiquity, and is divided into three branches, though in many places the one man seems to have done the whole lot. The wet cooper made barrels to hold liquids, the dry cooper made kegs for dry goods, and the white cooper made pails, wash tubs, churns, bailers, open-topped tubs and other staved ware for dairy and household uses. It must be apparent that he was a valuable member of the maritime community. Again, his tools have been described in a

263

Herring Barrel Making

A cooper at work, Lowestoft, about 1900

number of books, but his place as one of the maritime craftsmen of the small coastal ports fully justifies his inclusion here. Coopers were also carried on most of the larger sailing vessels as part of the crew, and this went back a long way. In 1627 Captain Smith defined the duties of coopers in a ships crew: 'the cooper is to look to the Caske, Hoopes, and Twigs, to stave or repair buckets, baricoes, cans and steepe tubs'. No distinction was drawn between wet, dry and white coopering, and this was probably the case with most of the small cooperages along the coast. It also seems that the tinplate can so familiar to us today originated as a product of the cooper, but which he has since lost.

The main stages in making a barrel were stave shaping, trussing, topping, cleaning or clearing, and finally hooping. In the figures which follow I have worked roughly in this order, though the trussing tools are not fully shown.

THE FIGURES

Figures 118(a) and (b)   Broad axes, which were side axes with a blade of up to twelve inches long, set at a slight angle to the haft to aid the downward chopping of staves. These axes had no poll. They were used for splitting staves out of the timber and shaping them up ready for the jointer, and for roughing out barrel heads.

Figure 118(c)   A froe, fromard or splitting knife which was used by some coopers for splitting out staves. It was driven down with a beetle or mallet, and was more commonly found in use by the various craftsmen working mostly out in the woods and copses in the countryside.

Figures 118(d), (e) and (f)   These three knives were used in succession for shaping the staves. The draw knife smoothed them after the axe, and before bevelling. The backing knife shaped the curve on the back or outside of the staves, and the hollowing knife took out the inside curve. This might be done with the aid of a cooper's block or a shave horse.

Figure 119(a)   A shave horse, used for shaping the staves for small barrels. The stave was clamped at its lower end, and the knife pulled towards the worker, who sat on the right-hand end of the horse with his feet pushing on the lower bar of the clamp.

Figure 119(b)   The cooper's jointer, which was basically a long plane, set up at one end on a low trestle with the plane iron upwards. Staves

265

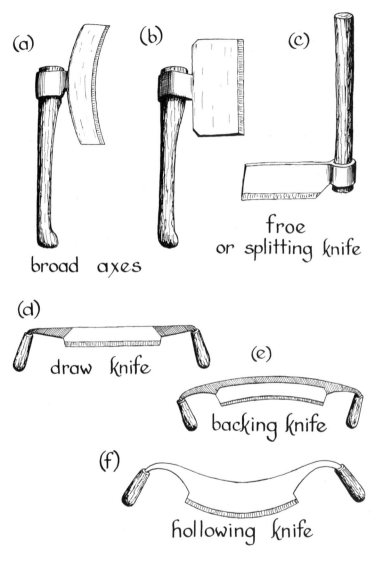

(a) (b) broad axes

(c) froe or splitting knife

(d) draw knife

(e) backing knife

(f) hollowing knife

Figure 118   The cooper

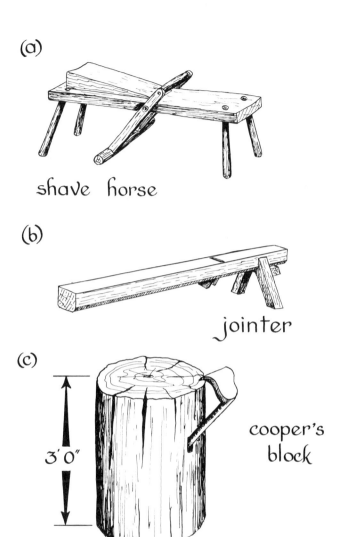

(a) shave horse

(b) jointer

(c) 3' 0" cooper's block

Figure 119   The cooper

(a)

clearing-out
or stoup plane

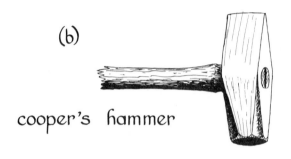

(b)

cooper's hammer

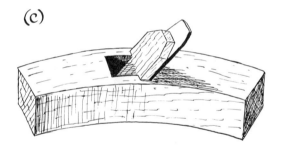

(c)

topping or sun plane

Figure 120   The cooper

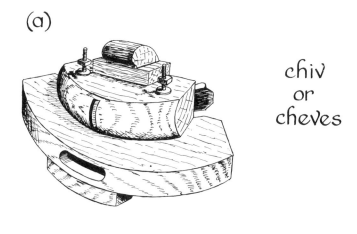

(a)

chiv
or
cheves

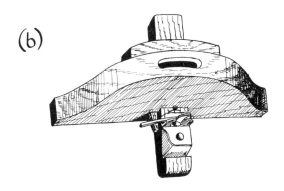

(b)

croze

Figure 121   The cooper

were bevelled by being pushed against the iron with a sweeping movement.

Figure 119(c)   The cooper's block on which staves were cut out, and with a hook driven into one side to grip the ends of long barrel staves too long for the shave horse for shaping.

Figure 120(a)   The stoup plane or clearing-out plane had a sole curved in two directions and a curved blade to clean out the inside curves of staves for small casks, water-breakers and the like, and was sometimes used for cleaning down the inside seams of the staves after trussing.

269

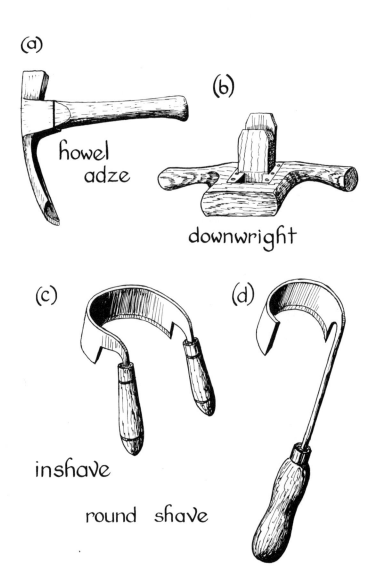

(a)

howel
adze

(b)

downwright

(c)

inshave

round shave

(d)

Figure 122 The cooper

Figure 120(b)   The cooper's hammer was almost a short-hafted sledge, but usually with a straight pein on one end of the head. It was usually about four or five pounds in weight.

Figure 120(c)   The sun or topping plane, used for finishing off the ends of the staves, presenting a smooth and even surface for the fence of the chiv and the croze to travel on in later stages.

Figure 121(a)   The chiv, cheves or cheeves was a kind of circular plane for cutting a shallow channel, known as the howel, below the top of the staves on the inside. The chiv was a late introduction, before this the howel adze was used to form the groove.

Figure 121(b)   The croze followed the chiv and formed the groove to hold the head in the howel.

Figure 122 (a)   The old howel adze, a short-hafted tool used for forming the howel before the chiv was devised. The cooper also used another short-hafted adze, shown in Figure 32(c), with a haft no more than nine inches long, for shaping inside the end of the cask (the chime) to produce a flat surface for the croze to run in.

Figure 122(b)   The downwright was a form of spokeshave with a slightly concave blade for cleaning up the outsides of barrels.

Figures 122(c) and (d)   The inshave and the round shave were both used for cleaning up the insides of barrels. Both had convex blades, and the long-handled round shave came in a series of sizes with either one or two handles.

Figures 123(a), (b), (c) and (d)   Various types of bits used by the cooper, used in the conventional type of woodworker's brace. The cooper also used a brace with a small fixed spoon bit for boring dowel holes for joining sections of the head, the bit being similar to *a*.

Figure 123(e)   The tapered tap borer or auger, for boring tap or bung holes. Sometimes the holes were cleaned up with a burning iron, which was rather like a soldering iron, after boring.

Figure 123(f)   A late development of the tap borer, in which a removable knife or cutter was used to cut a tapered hole with a rounded outer edge.

Figure 124(a)   The circular heading knife, used for producing the bevel on the edge of the head. The knife is bowed as well as curved, and the

271

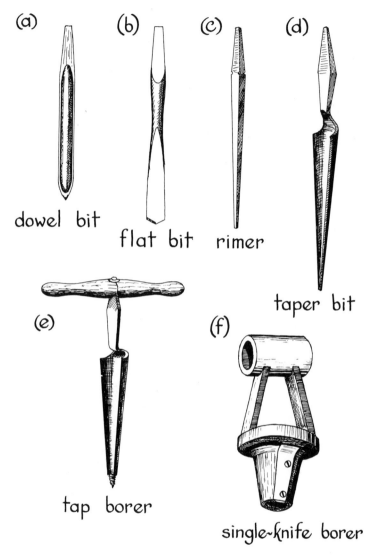

(a)

(b)

(c)

(d)

dowel bit

flat bit   rimer

taper bit

(e)

tap borer

(f)

single-knife borer

Figure 123   The cooper

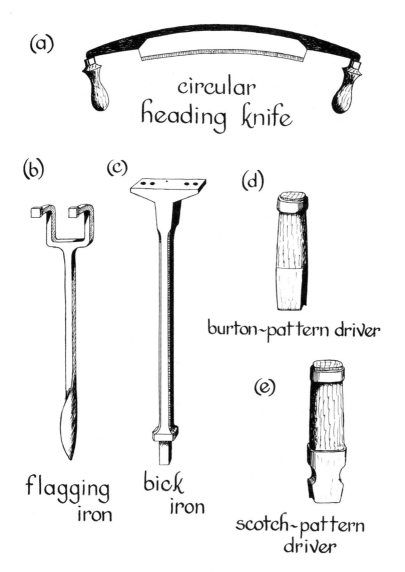

(a)

circular
heading knife

(b)

(c)

(d)

burton-pattern driver

(e)

flagging
iron

bick
iron

scotch-pattern
driver

Figure 124   The cooper

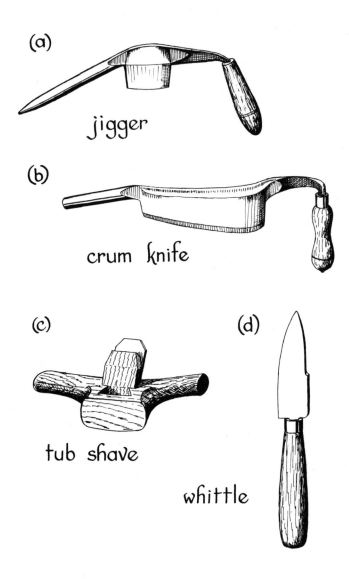

(a)

jigger

(b)

crum knife

(c)

tub shave

(d)

whittle

Figure 125   The cooper

substance of the metal is far thinner than that in a drawknife.

Figure 124(b)   The flagging iron, with which the joints between the staves were twisted open to insert the rushes used to make the joints tight.

Figure 124 (c)   The bick or beak iron, sometimes called a cooper's stake. It was used mainly for riveting hoops, the holes in the face taking the rivet shanks as they were hammered through.

Figures 124(d) and (e)   Two widely-used patterns of drivers or drifts for hammering down hoops. These were about six inches long, and seldom found with the original oak hafts, with a grooved iron end about three inches wide.

Figures 125(a) and (b)   The jigger and crum knife were used in repairing barrels and casks, the jigger being designed to recut the howel.

Figure 125(c) is a small version of the downwright, used on tubs and small staved ware.

Figure 125(d) is a cooper's whittle, a stubby straight-bladed knife, firmly handled. It served the cooper in many ways, just as the carpenter uses a knife for many purposes.

There were a few other tools which I should mention, though they have not been illustrated. For trussing a set of truss hoops were kept, made of ash, and in sizes to suit the work commonly carried out in the cooperage. A thick iron truss hoop was also used. The cresset was an iron basket grate, about a foot high and eight or nine inches in diameter, in which a fire of shavings was made to aid the trussing of the barrel. The barrel was inverted over the cresset. A scraper shave known as a buzz, which was sometimes no more than a flat steel blade, was used for finishing the outsides after working over with the downwright. A small knife with a blade set so that the cutting edge was nearly at right-angles to the handle, and known as a thief, was used to trim away rough edges inside the bunghole. Compasses were used to measure and mark out the head of the barrel. Another tool similar to a downwright, a heading swift or swifter, with an iron $2\frac{1}{2}$in wide, was used for the final smoothing of the head. It planed against the grain. A chincing iron was used to push in dried rushes or flags between sections of the head, and between the head and the howel groove. It was often home-made, from hoop iron, in the form of a small chisel. The heads were levered into position by an iron bar of about 1in diameter, bent at one end, which was called a jumper. The bent end allowed it to be worked up through the bung hole to lever the head up if it should drop below the groove. For driving down the end or chime hoops of a barrel a wooden baton known as a chime maul was used. This was generally made of oak, and about two feet or so long.

The tinsmith often doubled as a coppersmith in many of the smaller ports, and indeed their work was rather similar. The introduction of tinplate led many former coppersmiths to turn their hands to tinsmithing, making a tremendous range of cheaper and lighter products. In any port they could be found making tin kettles, teapots, oil cans, lamps, stove pipes, saucepans, boxes and tin trunks. Returning to their original craft, they also made those brass or copper windvanes known as 'wifts' for ship's mastheads. The working of these sheet metals consists mainly of hammering the metal to shape, stretching it, folding it for seams or edges, riveting and planishing. Seams were folded and soldered. To produce the variety of shapes a whole range of tools, hammers and shaping dies of a bewildering variety were used, and what follows is of necessity only a selection.

THE FIGURES

Figures 126(a), (b), (c), (d), (e), (f), (g), (h) and (i)   Hammers of different types.
Figure 126(j)   An anvil tool for forming grooves, though it is said to have been used in a wooden handle for forming with a light hammer.
Figure 126(k)   A hollow punch used for punching out round holes, such as might be required to fit a teapot spout.
Figures 126 (l) and (m)   A rivet set and snap, the set for driving the rivet into, keeping the sheet metal tight, and the snap for closing the rivet.

Figure 127(a)   The folding bar was for folding the edges of a straight sheet for either a simple bend or to start a folded seam.
Figures 127(b), (c), (d), (e), (f) and (g)   Forms of anvil or stake for producing different shapes. There are many varieties, many being named after some specific function, such as the teapot neck stake, others from their shape, such as the hatchet stake.

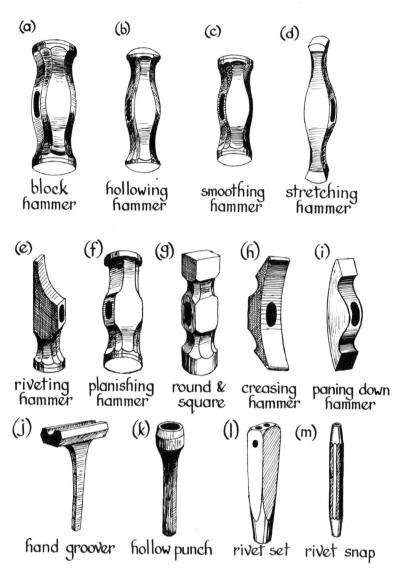

(a) block hammer

(b) hollowing hammer

(c) smoothing hammer

(d) stretching hammer

(e) riveting hammer

(f) planishing hammer

(g) round & square

(h) creasing hammer

(i) paning down hammer

(j) hand groover

(k) hollow punch

(l) rivet set

(m) rivet snap

Figure 126   The tinsmith

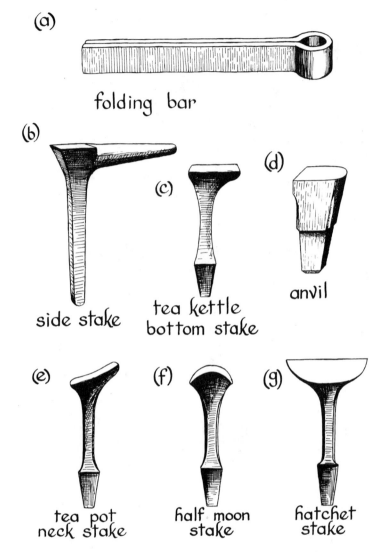

(a)

folding bar

(b)

side stake

(c)

tea kettle
bottom stake

(d)

anvil

(e)

tea pot
neck stake

(f)

half moon
stake

(g)

hatchet
stake

Figure 127   The tinsmith

Figures 128(a), (b), (c) and (d) show more stakes, three of which are named from their basic purposes.

Figure 128(e) The bick iron was also a form of stake, though not like the cooper's bick iron. The taper here was ideally suited for things like oil cans, deck flare spouts and so on.

Figure 128(f) The mandrel was a heavier tool than the ones shown so far. It was used for heavy bending, being gripped in a vice or clamped down to a heavy bench, and the metal was formed over and round it.

Figures 129(a) and (b) Two forms of shears used by the tinsmith. The stock shears were used in the hands, the block shears set up in a vice and only one arm was operated by hand.

Figure 129(c) The tinman's mallet was sometimes of box wood, or beech in the cheaper qualities, and used when a metal hammer might cause damage, such as large bends in sheets.

Figures 129(d) and (e) Two forms of the most common types of soldering irons used. That in (d) is probably the more common of the two, but there are plenty of the hatchet shape about still.

The coppersmith's trade has always struck me as being a most unhealthy one, if the fumes from hot copper are any guide. This may be why so many of them turned over to tinplate when the opportunity came along.

The maritime communities also included tradesmen such as the ship chandlers, who stocked the products of most of the smaller craftsmen. The chandlers had a most distinctive shop sign, but one which is seldom seen today. It was like, and is often mistaken for, a ships figurehead, always of a woman and always holding a purse in her hand. At one time this sign was in almost universal use, but it has long gone out of fashion. The last one I recall seeing was over a furniture shop in Dartmouth, Devon, which at one time had been a ship chandlers. Some years ago the then owner sold it, fully convinced that it was a ship's figurehead.

Mention of figureheads brings in a final craftsman, the figurehead carver, and a most elusive one he has proved. I have not illustrated any of his tools, since he used the normal range of woodcarver's chisels and gouges, with the round mallet so beautifully adapted for wood carving, and a few saws. Some figureheads are said to have been roughed out with various kinds of adze. The surviving—if that is the right word—

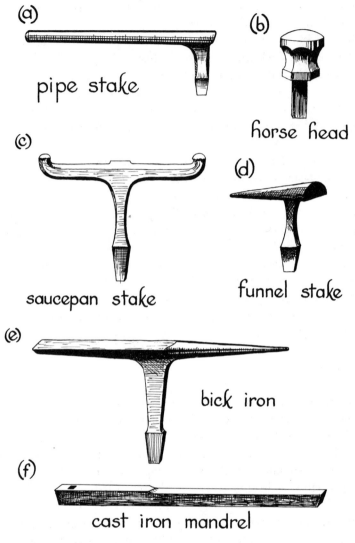

(a) pipe stake

(b) horse head

(c) saucepan stake

(d) funnel stake

(e) bick iron

(f) cast iron mandrel

Figure 128   The tinsmith

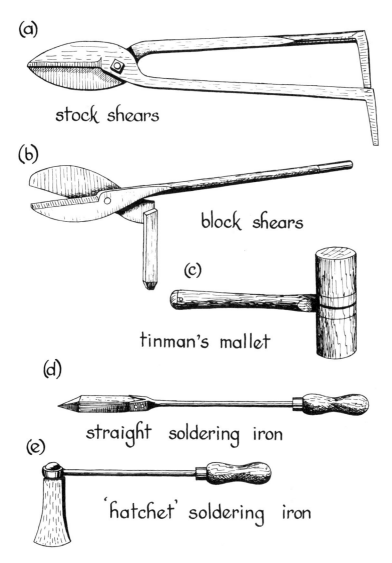

(a)

stock shears

(b)

block shears

(c)

tinman's mallet

(d)

straight soldering iron

(e)

'hatchet' soldering iron

Figure 129   The tinsmith

craftsmen are not of the traditional school. Most have taken it up as a new demand has arisen for this kind of work, with a break of about half a century in between. What information I have been able to glean suggests that the figurehead carver was an itinerant worker, moving from yard to yard, or working at one place on orders for a very wide area. I know of carvers who had workshops at rather widely separated places, working for shipyards over a large district. One of these was at Plymouth, another was at Southampton and another worked at Bideford, but not so many names have come down the years. In the Clyde Valley there was a guild of carvers—the Guild of Itinerant Carvers—who worked from shipyard to shipyard in that prolific shipbuilding area during the last century, but what became of their records, if any, I have not yet discovered. The decoration of ships, from figurehead to ginger-bread, is a fascinating subject and one which has not yet really been studied fully, and as a craft it must have employed many men at one time or another. But they remain extremely elusive people. Some were very shy men, who would not allow anyone to see them at work, and the impression I have gained is that they were regarded with a certain awe, as if they possessed some special magic. Perhaps this is appropriate, for their calling had a very long history, rooted in the days when the occulus of a vessel was expected to see and warn of hidden dangers. The occulus, the eye which even today appears on vessels in the Mediterranean, was supposedly endowed with magical powers.

Indeed, as one looks back over some of the tools used by many branches of the maritime trades, one is inclined to believe that the figurehead carver was not the only craftsman to possess magical powers.

APPENDICES

1 TIMBERS

It would be impossible to enumerate all the types and varieties of timber which have been and are used in shipbuilding, since the country of origin of the ship or vessel concerned dictates very largely the kind of timber used. It is said, for example, that certain parts of Greece were completely denuded of olive trees for shipbuilding purposes as early as Classical Greek times. Yet olive is not one of the woods found in Northern European or American shipbuilding, and certainly for some centuries these have been the main centres of ship production.

Timber is classified into two basic types—hardwoods and softwoods. This, however, does not necessarily grade the timbers as to hardness or softness, but is an indication of their individual structure. Balsa, for example, probably the softest timber known, is in fact a hardwood, having a grain structure similar to mahogany.

Timber was measured in different ways in the past. A load was approximately 50 cubic feet, while a cord was 128 cubic feet of stacked logs. This could be 8ft by 4ft by 4ft, 16ft by 4ft by 2ft or any other convenient stack. Other expressions were used for various sizes, such as 'thick stuff', which was over 4in thick and up to and over 12in wide; 'plank', which was in thicknesses from 1½in to 4in; and 'boards', which were under 1½in thick. Thinner planking was sometimes referred to as 'wainscot'.

Oak. English oak was said to be the strongest and most durable variety. Its strong grain and high density sometimes made it rather difficult to work, yet it was always the great favourite among English shipbuilders. American oak is less durable than English, coarser in the grain, and was usually used only for inferior work. It is rather lighter in colour than English oak (which is a light brown), and it is often described as 'silver grained'. Austrian oak is a useful straight-grained timber which shows a good 'figure' when cut into boards. It also works easily, and its colour is a light brown. Danzig or Polish oak has a close straight grain with bright rays. It is very elastic, moderately durable, and dark brown in colour. Riga or Russian oak is rather similar to Danzig, with a very fine figure.

283

Most of the imported oaks, especially those from Europe, arrived in half-round logs.

All oak has a high content of gallic acid, which rapidly corrodes unprotected iron and steelwork. All such metal coming into contact with oak is therefore commonly galvanised, or brass or copper is used. The same chemical action causes serious black or blue-black staining in the oak which rots out in way of unprotected fastenings. This trouble did not arise when ships were fastened mainly with treenails. The weight of seasoned oak is approximately 48lb per cubic foot.

Elm. English elm is a fibrous, dense and tough timber which bears the driving of nails without splitting. It is very durable under water, though this durability is not so marked when used under changing conditions. Although an open-grained timber, the contortions of the fibres in its structure give it great toughness. Its colour is a reddish brown, and its seasoned weight about 38lb per cubic foot.

American elm is also very tough and close-grained, being rather denser than the English variety. It is very durable and used extensively for battens, fenders and other places which take considerable wear.

Canadian Rock Elm is a very heavy, dense timber, imported in some quantities during World War II for the construction of wooden non-magnetic minesweepers. Very strong and durable.

Pitchpine Sometimes called Southern Pine, pitchpine is a resinous timber, straight-grained and reasonably free from knots, with distinct annual rings. It suffers from a high rate of shrinkage, but is fairly durable when exposed to the weather. There are two varieties, the long-leaved being considered the superior. It has a fine texture and is very dense and strong. Pitchpine is grown mostly in the southern states of the USA, and it has a seasoned weight of approximately 50lb per cubic foot.

Northern Pine. Also known as Red Deal, this is a resinous wood, straight-grained, rather knotty and with distinct annual rings. It is easy to work, soft and rather pliant, but quite durable in exposed positions. Used mainly for grounds and for some deck planking. Seasoned weight about 35lb per cubic foot.

Yellow Pine. Sometimes called White Pine, this is soft textured and straight-grained, with a rather yellowish colour. Narrow resin ducts show up in the grain as thin dark lines or dashes. It grows mainly in Canada and the north-eastern parts of the USA. Yellow pine works very easily, though it is not very strong. At one time, when supplies were plentiful, it was very extensively used in furniture-making, covered by veneers, and was found in the furnishings of ships' cabins, especially in drawer and cupboard backs. Today it is mainly used for constructional half-models and in patternmaking for iron or brass founding. When properly seasoned it is very stable, resisting warping fairly well and altering shape very little. The seasoned weight is about 25lb per cubic foot.

Kauri Pine. Coming from New Zealand, this is even textured and has a smooth surface. It is free of resin canals, and the annual rings are barely visible. It formerly grew to very great size, and often one single tree was sufficient to provide a dugout basis for an enormous Maori canoe. It is light, strong and very durable. Since New Zealand is the only source of this timber, it is somewhat expensive elsewhere.

Douglas Fir. This Fir, which is known as Oregon pine or British Columbian pine, depending upon where grown, is one of the most important of all the commercial timbers, and probably one of the most widely used. Reddish in colour, it has a fairly coarse texture with visible rings and resin ducts, though the medullary rays are invisible. It can be obtained in very large sizes, is durable and very strong, though not so long-lasting in use as pitchpine.

Teak, Burma or Indian. A weather resisting, durable and difficult to work timber. It contains an oil that not only preserves ironwork, but also gives it a good degree of resistance to insect infestation. It is a straight-grained timber with a rather unpleasant odour when being worked. The pores of the wood contain a gritty substance, possibly dried globules of resin, which very quickly blunt the tools being used to work it. It is a pleasant brown colour, and the seasoned weight is about 42lb per cubic foot.

Iroko. Known as 'African teak', mvule, odum, kambala, depending upon its area of origin, this West African timber was introduced as a substitute for teak during World War II, though not able to replace it completely. It is a strong timber though not quite as strong and durable as teak. It is brown in colour, very close to the colour of teak, and is considered by many shipbuilders to be the best of the West African teak substitutes. Today it is well recognised and used in its own right as a shipbuilding timber.

Afrormosia. Another African timber that is sometimes used as a substitute for teak, but it does not possess the same degree of strength. Some yacht decks have been laid with it, but it suffers from a tendency to bleach when subjected to combined exposure to seawater and sunlight, and is rumoured to be slightly suspect in respect of stability.

European or Common Spruce. This timber, which is sometimes known as whitewood, has a coarse texture, and is whitish in colour. The sapwood and heartwood are indistinguishable. It is grown mostly in North Russia, Scandinavia and the Baltic countries. It is fairly strong, with a straight grain, and is used mainly for joinery and constructional work, but does not compare very favourably with the spruce grown in the North American continent.

American Spruce. The timber is rather better than the European variety and there are several varieties. Although similar to European spruce, it is harder and can be obtained in larger sizes. The most valuable qualities are said to be those from Quebec and West Virginia.

Sitka Spruce. Sometimes known as silver spruce, this is grown in the United States, mainly in Washington and Oregon, and also in British Columbia. Its great strength makes it a very valuable timber. The annual rings are very narrow and close, and it possesses great shock-resisting qualities. Lower grades are used in contructional and joinery work, but the

285

finest qualities are in great demand for aircraft construction and for the stringers of light, fast small vessels. Indeed, many clench-built craft are planked with silver spruce.

Sequoia. Also known as Giant Redwood or Californian Redwood, timber is cut from trees of tremendous size. It is a soft-textured wood, of a rich red colour, and very straight-grained owing to the great height attained by the trees. As a timber it is extremely durable, light in weight and free of resin. It can stand very adverse weather conditions and is resistant to insect infestation, particularly termites. It is used in Britain for several purposes such as vat making, tunnel building and a certain amount of external railway constructional work, but I have no record of its having been used in shipbuilding.

TIMBERS USED IN MASTING

The strength requirements of masting timbers led to the acceptance of certain standards for this purpose. Elm, for example, was selected from trees felled between November and February, since it contains no sap. Its purpose in masting was for caps, bibbs, bees and parts of the tops. The relative strengths of fir were regarded in various ways which are rather difficult to follow. Fir from Riga and Gothenburg was considered to be about one tenth stronger than Norway fir, and about one sixth stronger than New England fir. Scots fir was also considered stronger than Norway fir, but by how much I have not been able to discover. On the other hand, the largest trees were those from New England.

TIMBERS USED IN COOPERAGE

The most important timber used in this craft was that known as 'stave woods', for obvious reasons. Oak was chosen for this purpose, but of a rather special quality. Until about 1840 imported narrow planks of oak from the Baltic coast of Germany, known as 'clapboard', was used. These were riven planks, thick on one edge and thin on the other from being riven through from the outside to the heart of the log. Riven in this manner the natural medullary rays of the oak lay parallel to the face, producing a more waterproof timber less prone to seepage. An Act of Parliament of 1833 described clapboard rather neatly as 'wood staves not above 3 inches thick, or 7 inches breadth, or 63 inches long'. The oak chosen was a quick-growing one which never really matured or was not allowed to mature. After cutting it 'case-hardened' and continued to expand. Round about 1840, however, timbers with similar qualities were found in the Colonies, and as these started to be imported so the German oak was gradually excluded. The Colonial 'stave-woods' included *Quassia simaruba* from Jamaica, *Simaruba amara* from the West Indies and *Sterculia foetida* from Australia, East Africa and the East Indies. During the great heyday of the West Country pilchard trade in South Devon, from about 1480

286

onwards for some three to four centuries, there were vast imports of both salt and barrel staves from the Biscay ports. Presumably these staves would be of a similar material to that used for the French wine barrels and hogsheads.

2 SAILCLOTHS

Sailcloths have been made of many materials, and new synthetic fibres have brought about many changes. The Romans and Celts are believed to have used animal hides, but in more recent times the mainstay of the sailing fleets was flax.

Flax (Linum usitatissimum). The tough staple, which can be some 4in or more, is separated from the stems by the process known as retting. It is coarser than cotton and rather difficult to spin very fine. It has the advantage of being some 20 per cent stronger when wet than when dry, and when wet it is quite soft to handle. Although suited to hard use, and still chosen today for some storm sails, it has a tendency to pull out of shape. Even so, it is stronger than cotton. In spite of its wet strength, if it is allowed to remain wet for any length of time it can develop mildew.

Cotton. Believed to have come into Europe first through Spain (where it was known as *coton*), then France, cotton probably first appeared as sails in Europe on the racing schooner *America* when she visited British waters in 1851. With her sails lying much flatter than the sagging flax used by her rivals she could lie much closer to the wind, and her victories over her British opponents are now almost legendary.

The staple of cotton is produced by the process known as ginning, in which the cotton seed is separated from the lint. The staple is shorter and finer than flax, seldom being more than one inch long, but its woolly, twisted texture causes great resistance between the fibres when spun into a thread. The cloth it produces is uniform, and its thread, and consequently the cloth, is finer than flax. The closeness of the weave meant a great increase in sail efficiency. Cotton was usually produced in sail widths from 12in up to 54in, but the most common today is 36in.

Nylon. One of the man-made fibres, nylon is a polyamide plastic in fibre form and is derived from coal. Although developed in the USA from 1932 onwards, it was not used for sails until after World War II, when suitable mass-production methods had been devised. It has an inherent elasticity, which has prevented it being used for many types of rope, but for certain sails such as spinnakers and some light reaching sails it is ideal. It is not affected by mildew, but it is weakened by too long exposure to sunlight. It is produced in widths of only 18in, intended primarily for making yacht sails.

Polyester or polyethylene terephthalate. Another of the man-made artificial fibres, which is commonly marketed by ICI under the registered trade name of terylene, polyester was invented by Whinfield and Dickson, of the

Calico Printers' Association, Lancashire, England, in 1941. Development was delayed due to World War II, but in 1944 ICI were able to produce it for the first time. Since licences started to expire in 1967 there has been a free market in the yarn, and it is produced on a world-wide scale. Gowen & Co., of Essex, England, made the first British terylene sails in the winter of 1951–2 for the 8-metre yacht *Sonda*. The yarn has no staple, being manufactured in one continuous filament. Several of these filaments twisted together form the thread. To give the required finishes (hard, soft, etc) special finishing is called for, such as heat-relaxing and filling with various resin fillers. The best terylene sailcloth has no fillers or additives, but is a specially woven material. Since 1964 the well-known British sailmakers, Ratsey & Lapthorn, have woven their own sailcloth of terylene in widths which vary from about 32in to 36in, depending upon the amount of shrinkage induced during heat treatment.

Polypropylene. Another ICI product sold in England under the name of ulstron, which, as sailcloth, has very high tenacity, a low density and a very low moisture absorbtion rate, and is very tough. However, it suffers far more than nylon from deterioration due to exposure to sunlight.

Melinex. Producing faster sails than terylene, this man-made material has a nil moisture absorbtion rate. It is a resin-glass or glass-fibre based material, but so far its disadvantage is that it tends to fail due to poor flexibility. Once this difficulty can be solved no doubt this will prove a highly successful sailcloth.

Meanwhile, new materials are always being developed, and even before these notes are in print there will probably be several new types of sailcloth both experimental and in production.

SIZES OF FLAX CANVAS

Flax canvas sailcloth was commonly made in bolts of 40 yards, 24 inches wide. It was known by numbers which corresponded with the weight in pounds per bolt. Although the standard width was 24 inches, a narrower width of 18 inches was produced for strong jibs and drivers.

No 1—46lb per bolt	No 5—34lb per bolt
No 2—43lb per bolt	No 6—31lb per bolt
No 3—40lb per bolt	No 7—28lb per bolt
No 4—37lb per bolt	No 8—25lb per bolt

Admiralty specifications laid down that Nos 1, 2 and 3 canvases should be composed of at least 560 double threads of yarn, both warp and weft to be of long-staple flax with no admixture of tow whatever. It seems that some of the more unscrupulous sailcloth manufacturers tended to mix tow with some of their cheaper grades of sailcloth.

Again the Admiralty laid down specifications, which, incidentally, were often later adaptations of the standards usually expected by merchant shipmasters. I say shipmasters in preference to ship owners, since many owners were parsimonious to a point close to criminal negligence when it came to equipping their ships. The fact that men's lives might depend on the saving of a few coppers per bolt of sailcloth did not always matter.

Sewing twine as chosen by most good sailmakers was made of flax, of 3 folds, spun up to produce between 360 and 430 fathoms per pound. One pound of twine was expected to sew 160 yards—4 bolts—of flax canvas.

Waxed twine was preferred for many sails, helping not only to preserve the twine, but making sewing easier. Twine used for sewing large sails for use in the Royal Navy was waxed by hand. For sewing canvasses nos 1, 2, 3 and 4, the twine was waxed with genuine beeswax mixed with a sixth part of clear turpentine. For canvasses nos 5, 6, 7 and 8, the twine was dipped in a compound made from 4lb of beeswax, 5lb of tallow and 1lb of clear turpentine. Roping twine was also dipped in the second formula, while merchant service twine was dipped in tar softened with a proportion of oil.

Later twines, of course, of a variety of man-made materials, are now in common use. Terylene seems to be the most popular at the moment. It is very strong and stable, but no doubt it too will be superseded in due course by some even more efficient material.

3 ROPE MATERIALS AND ROPEMAKING

Rope has been made from a tremendous variety of materials since its manufacture first started. Natural ropes, such as twisted lianas and creepers, may have been adequate in very primitive times or where they were prolific, but these conditions did not always apply. The Egyptians made ropes from flax, papyrus, palm fibre, leather, rawhide and probably other materials. In England the list of materials included not only the familiar hemp and flax, but nettles, brambles, willow bark and lime tree bark. The following notes cover those materials more commonly known and used in the industry.

Hemp (Cannabis sativa). Hemp seems to have been the most popular and, although a relative of the common stinging nettle, it is really a native of India and Persia. This is the true hemp, and it has long been cultivated primarily for ropeworking in Europe, USSR, Japan and Korea. The Italian-grown hemp is still used in ropes and twines where strength is important, followed in quality by Russian and Hungarian hemp. The cultivation of true hemp is prohibited in many places, since it is the source of hashish, marijuana and cannabis.

There are a number of other plants often grouped together under the name of hemp, none of which are true hemps, but all of which are used in varying degrees in the making of rope. The most common are :

Sunn hemp (India)
Bowstring hemp (tropical Africa and Asia)
New Zealand Hemp or Flax (New Zealand and St Helena)
Pita hemp (Columbia)
Mauritius hemp
Manilla hemp (Philippine Islands)
Henequen (Caribbean, Mexico, Cuba)
Sisal (East and West Africa, Central and South America)
Bombay hemp (India)
Ramie
Egyptian cotton
Maguey (Philippine Islands)

Hemp and the other hemp-type fibres are classified as 'hard' or 'soft', depending upon their natural texture. Typical of the hard hemps are sisal, manilla, henequen, Mauritius hemp and New Zealand hemp. Of the soft hemps true hemp and sunn hemp are typical.

Some ropemakers bought their hemp ready made up into spunyarn, and worked it up into rope from that state.

Flax (Linum usitatissimum). Although it was cultivated in two forms, both are recognised under the same botanical nomenclature. One produced long-staple fibres for ropes and sailcloth, the other was for its seed (linseed).

Jute. Grown in India, jute is used especially for the cores of some types of wire ropes.

Cotton. Usually coming from Egypt, cotton was made into ropes as well as cloth. It is soft and bends easily, and because of this flexibility was much favoured for driving ropes and belts. It is also said to make the best clothes lines.

Manilla. Mostly grown in the Philippine Islands, and to a lesser degree in Japan, it is strong and does not absorb water easily. It is made from the stem of a plant of the banana family, known by the native name of abaca. It was frequently specified for the lifeboat davit falls on steamers, though it may well now have given way to a synthetic fibre. Some is also grown in Java.

Sisal (Agave rigida elongata). Cheaper than manilla, but not quite as good, sisal needs chemical treatment to prevent it absorbing water. It is mostly grown in the provinces of Yucatan, Campeche and Sinaloc in Mexico, parts of South America, Java, Hawaii, and Bahamas, the West Indies and East Africa. At the time of the Spanish conquest of Mexico it was found already in use by the natives there, and referred to as cordage fibre.

New Zealand hemp. Softer than sisal, and both strong and supple.

Maguey (Agave americana or cantala). Produced in the Philippine Islands and a relative of the more common sisal.

290

Coir Made from the shorter fibres of the outer coverings of coconuts. The husks are removed before the nuts are quite ripe and soaked in salt water for several months before being beaten to separate the fibres. Coir yarn is twisted into a continuous yarn by hand in the country of origin, and sold to the ropemakers in made-up skeins. Most of it comes from Céylon and India. Coir is very light, though not so strong as sisal or manilla. Its special qualities are high resistance to water absorbtion and great resilience, allowing it to stand up to sudden jerks. This makes it extremely useful for towing, and it is used also for fenders and matting.

Synthetic fibres. There are a number of new synthetics on the market today, and new ones seem to appear almost daily. Nylon is a very useful one; it has nearly twice the strength of manilla for a given size, it is light, and does not swell in water. However, it has considerable elasticity under load, and this makes it unsuitable for some purposes. Rayon was one of the first of the synthetics fibres to be used for ropemaking. This was developed in England early in the twentieth century, and was once favoured for whale harpoon lines, but has now been superseded. Other synthetics have various qualities and characteristics which suit them for certain purposes.

Hard natural fibres are assessed for strength in relation to the strongest, manilla, at a nominal 100; thus sisal has a relative strength of 86, New Zealand hemp 85, istle 62 and Mauritius hemp 33.

TYPES OF ROPES AND LINES PRODUCED IN BRITAIN

A very wide range of ropes and twines were once produced in the rope and twine walks of Britain. Today's list must be considerably smaller. The following were common in the nineteenth century and the early twentieth century :

Boltrope twine
Cod line, 18-thread, 15-thread, 12-thread and 9-thread
Cork lines
Deep-sea lines, 18-thread, 12-thread, 9-thread
Dolphin lines, 12-thread
Drum lines, 16-thread
Drum fish lines, 9-thread
Foregauger, 3 strands x 48 threads each
Hambro' line, 12-thread, 9-thread, 6-thread
Hammock line, 3-thread
Hand lead line, 12-thread
House line, 3-thread
Jack line, 9-thread
Lead rope
Log lines, 12-thread, 9-thread, 6-thread
Mackerel line, 6-thread
Marline, 2-thread
Sash line, 4-strand

Seal twine, 12-thread
Seaming twine, 2-thread, 3-thread
Sean or seine lines, 18-thread
Spunyarn, 2-, 3-, 4-yarn
Store twine, 2-thread
Turtle twine, 3-thread
Topt twine, 3-strand
Whale lines, 3-strand x 24 threads each
Whipping twine
Whiting lines, 6-thread
Worming, 2-, or 3-strand.

In all this list there is no mention of anything so common as 'string', for the seaman, and indeed the rope and twine maker, rarely used the word. Those who made what we call string called themselves twine makers.

In addition to the various forms of cordage listed, there were many others such as trawl warps, ratlines, grass towing warps, cables and hawsers of all sizes and types. The largest cable in any sailing ship was the great hemp sheet-anchor cable. The cable was of 3 strands, each strand made of 3 ropes, each rope of 3 twists or strands. In a first rate ship of the line in the 1840s the anchor itself weighed 90cwt or 10,080lb. The following table of sizes and weights of hemp sheet-anchor cables is based on coils of 120 fathoms each. The common use at sea of the 'cable' as a measurement of distance is, or was, precisely this—120 fathoms or 720ft.

Circumference	Threads (4lb each)	Weight per coil
3in	48	192lb
5in	121	484lb
10in	485	1,940lb
15in	1,093	4,372lb
20in	1,943	7,772lb

4 MASTING

Large masts were built up from a series of pieces coaked and bolted together. Each piece had its own name.

Spindle or upper tree. In large masts usually made of two trees, coaked into each other along the centre line and bolted at 5ft intervals. The spindle tapered at both ends. Small spindles were made from a single tree.

Side trees. Two in each mast, each with heel pieces. Again in large masts each side tree might be in two parts, coaked together and bolted at 10ft intervals. Small side trees were in one piece. These were coaked into the lower tongue or taper of the spindle, and below that into each other, then bolted all through at 5ft intervals.

Heel pieces. Short lengths scarphed to the lower part of the side trees to make up length. They were often worked short in order to gain substance in the middle.

Side fishes. Long fir planks let in and coaked into the flat surface formed by the side trees and spindle. The fishes were thick enough to gain on the fore and aft diameter. The thwartships diameter was gained by the spindle and side trees. At this stage the mast was rounded up and secured by iron hoops driven on.

Cheeks. Made of large fir, at one time of oak, these were coaked or tabled into the upper taper or tongue of the spindle, thick enough to fashion out the head of the mast and leave a stop to support the trestle-trees. These were bolted together and secured by iron hoops on the squared head.

Front fish or paunch. A long plank of fir, hollowed to fit the round of the mast, fastened on the foreside of the mast over the iron hoops.

Cant pieces and fillings. Various pieces of fir fitted as needed to fill spaces. Cant pieces make good the angles left between the side trees and side fishes to form a fair round with the side of the mast and the upper part of the front fish. The whole was then strongly woolded together between every hoop, using 13 close turns of rope, each turn being secured by special woolding nails with leather washers under their heads to prevent cutting into the rope.

Smaller masts were often made out of two trees, an upper and a lower. These were scarphed and coaked together in the middle, the upper part forming a tongue for the cheeks to fit. The lower tree, with the addition of a heel piece to make good the length of the upper tree, gave the fore and aft diameter. Two side fishes were added, the mast hooped, and the cheeks let on.

5 COOPER'S BARRELS

There are certain traditional types of barrel produced by coopers, but the standards for them have not always been the same. At various times standards were laid down by Act of Parliament or by Royal Edict, but even the gallonage has changed in the course of time. Nevertheless, the following list is given as a guide to the principal sizes and types of traditional barrel.

TRADITIONAL BARREL TYPES

Barrels were given such names as hogshead, butt, tun, pipe, Queen's pipe, puncheon, firkin, keeve, kier, tub, tierce, vat and kilderkin.

The hogshead was fixed in 1423 at 63 old wine gallons, which is the equivalent of $52\frac{1}{2}$ imperial gallons.

A wine barrel in the days of Richard II was declared to contain $31\frac{1}{2}$ gallons, presumably again old wine gallons.

Barrels to contain eels or herrings, in the time of Henry VI, were set at 30 gallons.

Ale and beer barrels were set at various capacities during the reign of Henry VIII, and the differences, though close, are rather curious. London ale barrels should contain 32 beer gallons, as distinct from old or new wine gallons, while a London beer barrel would hold 36 gallons. Country ale and beer barrels were set at the same capacity, 34 gallons.

A little later we find that a barrel of vinegar should contain 34 gallons, a barrel for soap should hold 30 gallons, a barrel for salmon and spruce beer 42 gallons, and a barrel of honey or codfish 32 gallons.

Two further sizes were legalised in 1765, by which time some of the earlier types had probably fallen out of use, though since both the new types were for fish this does not by any means follow. The 1765 barrels were for fresh fish, to hold 38 wine gallons, and for salt fish, to hold 50 gallons.

6 BASKETRY

The prepared osiers used by basketmakers have been given various traditional names, here listed in order of size :

Luke or tack
Short-small
Long-small
Threepenny
Middleboro
Great

The four main parts of each rod were known as butts, tops, bellies and backs.

STROKES USED IN BASKETRY

Slew. Two or more rods woven in together.

Rand. One rod worked alternatively in front of and behind each stick—the stick being the vertical rod.

Pair. Two rods woven alternatively one under the other forming a kind of twisted weave.

Wale. Three or more worked alternatively, one by one, in front of two, three or even more sticks, then behind one, to form a string course, sometimes called a building course.

Borders were of several types, the most used being known as common, plaited, roped, tracked and scalloped.

BASKET WILLOW OR OSIER

Good osier is not easy to obtain today, since most of the old beds have been either grubbed out for grazing land, filled and built over, or just left to stagnate, and they are not easy to recover. Osiers were grown from sets, which were the best shoots from a current year's growth, about seven or eight feet long, pushed into the ground about two feet, between December and March, at a rate of about 20,000 per acre. Normally they took three years to grow, though sometimes they were cut in the second season, whereas earlier it had been customary to cut in the third or fourth season. Proper management was absolutely essential. The osiers would then be cut once a year or perhaps if thicker rods were wanted once in two years, but if left later than that they become overgrown and are of very little further use.

White willow were the finest peeled osier rods. Buff or red willow was dyed by boiling for about six hours before removing the peel, or sometimes by steaming in pipes set at an angle containing water and with the lower end plugged. The best willows produced straight peeled rods about 12ft in length. Coarse basketry rods were sold as they were, green, unstripped and unseasoned.

SELECT BIBLIOGRAPHY

Abell, Sir Westcott. *The Shipwright's Trade* (1948)

Arbman, Holger. *The Vikings* (Thames & Hudson, 1961)

Boyle, Vernon. 'Crafts of an Old Seaport', in *Trans of Devonshire Association,* vol 80 (1948)

Carter, H. R. *Rope, Twine and Thread Making* (1924)

Chapelle, Howard. *Boatbuilding* (Allen & Unwin 1941)

Dickinson, H. W. 'The Taylors of Southampton' in *Trans of the Newcomen Soc* vol XXIX

Encyclopaedia Britannica (9th edition)

Engineer's & Machinist's Assistant (1847)

Gilbert, K. R. *The Portsmouth Blockmaking Machinery* (1964)

Goodman, W. L. *A History of Woodworking Tools* (1964)

Greenhill, Basil. *The Merchant Schooner* (2 vols David & Charles, 1968)

Haarer, A. E. *Ropes and Ropemaking* (Oxford University Press, 1950)

Hennell, T. *The Countryman at Work* (1947)

Hogg, Garry. *Hammer & Tongs* (1964)

Holtzapffel, Charles. *Turning & Mechanical Manipulation* (1847)

Horne, R. S. *The Blockmills in H.M. Dockyard at Portsmouth* (1968)

Hughes, G. P. *Living Crafts* (1953)

Jenkins, J. Geraint. *Traditional Country Craftsmen* (Routledge & Kegan Paul, 1965)

Jobson, Allan. *Household & Country Crafts* (1953)

Kipping, Robert. *Sails & Sailmaking* (1904)

Knight, E. H. *The Practical Dictionary of Mechanics* (1877)

March, E. J. *Sailing Drifters* (David & Charles, 1969)

March, E. J. *Sailing Trawlers* (David & Charles, 1970)

Martyr, Weston. *Southseaman*

Mercer, Henry C. *Ancient Carpenter's Tools* (Pennsylvania, 1960)

Mitchell, G. Percy. *A Boatbuilder's Story* (Kingston Publications, 1969)

'The Norfolk Sailor', *Norfolk Naut Res Soc*, no 8 (1964)

Petrie, Sir W. Flinders. *Tools and Weapons* (1917; reprinted by Arisa Phillips, 1974)

Rees, A. *Cyclopaedia of Arts, Sciences and Literature,* vol XXI; plates vol II (1819)

Rogers, R. Inkerman. *Ships and Shipyards of Bideford,* (*c*1948)

Salaman, R. A. 'Tools of the Shipwright, 1650–1925', in *Folklife,* vol 5 (1967)

Smith, Joseph. *Explanation or Key to the various manufactories of Sheffield . . . for . . . Merchants, Wholesale Ironmongers and Travellers* (1816)

Steele, David. *The Elements and Practice of Rigging and Seamanship* (1794)

Sutherland, William. *The Shipbuilder's Assistant* (1711)

Wilkinson, Sir J. R. *The Ancient Egyptians* (2 vols, 1854)

Wilson, D. M. *The Anglo-Saxons* (Penguin Books, 1971)

Woods, K. S. *Rural Crafts of England* (E.P. 1947)

ACKNOWLEDGEMENTS

There are many other sources for the trades I have endeavoured to cover in this book, many of them fleeting hints which hardly warrant entry as separate sources. Having spent nearly twenty years in a shipyard in the West of England, I have acquired a considerable amount of information from former workmates whose names, even if I could remember them all, would take pages. My thanks must therefore go to all those old craftsmen of Dartmouth, Brixham, Salcombe, Falmouth, Plymouth and Teignmouth with whom I worked and talked, not then realising that one day I should be recalling those long-ago discussions.

INDEX

Page numbers in italic type indicate illustrations

299